The Essential Pocket Book of EMERGENCY CHEMICAL MANAGEMENT

David R. Quigley

T0132666

CRC Press

Boca Raton   New York   London   Tokyo

Library of Congress Cataloging-in-Publication Data

Quigley, D.R. (David R.)
    The essential pocket book of emergency chemical management / David R. Quigley.
        p.   cm.
    Includes index.
    ISBN 0-8493-8989-5 (alk. paper)
    1. Hazardous substances--Accidents--Management--Handbooks, manuals, etc. I. Title.
T55.3.H3Q53 1996
660′.2804—dc20   95-51495
                                                                                                              CIP

This book contains information obtained from authentic and highly regarded sources. Reprinted material is quoted with permission, and sources are indicated. A wide variety of references are listed. Reasonable efforts have been made to publish reliable data and information, but the author and the publisher cannot assume responsibility for the validity of all materials or for the consequences of their use.

Neither this book nor any part may be reproduced or transmitted in any form or by any means, electronic or mechanical, including photocopying, microfilming, and recording, or by any information storage or retrieval system, without prior permission in writing from the publisher.

CRC Press, Inc.'s consent does not extend to copying for general distribution, for promotion, for creating new works, or for resale. Specific permission must be obtained in writing from CRC Press for such copying.

Direct all inquiries to CRC Press, Inc., 2000 Corporate Blvd., N.W., Boca Raton, Florida 33431.

© 1996 by CRC Press, Inc.

No claim to original U.S. Government works
International Standard Book Number 0-8493-8989-5
Library of Congress Card Number 95-51495
Printed in the United States of America 1 2 3 4 5 6 7 8 9 0
Printed on acid-free paper

Table of Contents

How to Use This Book

About the Author

David R. Quigley, Ph.D., is the founder of D.R. Quigley and Associates, a company which specializes in chemical safety and emergency response. He is also an Advisory Scientist at the Idaho National Engineering Laboratory and an Adjunct Professor at both the University of Idaho and Idaho State University.

Dr. Quigley received his ACS Certified B.S. in chemistry from Florida Atlantic University in Boca Raton, Florida, and his M.S. and Ph.D. in chemistry from the University of Missouri—Rolla. He spent five years on the research faculty at the University of Colorado Health Sciences Center in Denver before moving to the Idaho National Engineering Laboratory.

A member of the American Chemical Society and the American Association for the Advancement of Science, Dr. Quigley has written approximately 60 research publications in the fields of biochemistry, organic chemistry, toxicology, and hazardous materials management. He has also presented numerous invited lectures in the United States and other countries.

Dr. Quigley has been active in chemical safety and has been an emergency responder for many years, aiding numerous emergency response and law enforcement organizations in southern Idaho.

HOW TO USE THIS BOOK

This book is meant to be an aid for the first responder to an incident. The first section contains general chemical information. Each entry is divided into numerous sections in an effort to provide first responders with as much information as possible in as little space as possible. These sections are:

Chemical Name. This column lists the common chemical name for the chemical in question. While each substance may have numerous names (many being "common"), only one name is used for the sake of brevity. If a "***" symbol appears, then the chemical is also listed in the book's second section, which contains information concerning the recommended DOT Take Cover and Isolation Distances as well as the RCRA Waste Number and Reportable Quantities.

DOT #. Each substance that is transported in quantity will have a Department of Transportation number associated with it that is posted on the outside of the carrier. These numbers are standardized and taken from DOT P 5800.5, and they can be used to identify the cargo. An index of DOT numbers is located in the back of this book.

CAS Number. Each chemical has a CAS (Chemical Abstract Services) Number. There is only one CAS Number for each substance; it can be used to accurately identify a substance when several pseudonyms are present.

Form. Form is a brief description of what the substance may look like. It should be kept in mind that the appearance of a particular substance may vary a great deal. A liquid that has a boiling point near ambient temperature may actually appear as a gas. Many substances may become discolored over time. Commonly used abbreviations are: C.=colorless; SOL.=solid; FUM.=fuming; LIQ.=liquid; YELL.=yellow; PURP.=purple. The numerical value appearing below liquids is the density of that liquid. Values less than one indicate that the substance is less dense than water and will float. Values greater than one indicate that the substance is denser than water and will tend to sink. A value equal to one indicates the substance will tend neither to sink nor float.

NFPA. These codes are defined by National Fire Protection Association (NFPA) standards 49 and 325M. Each three-digit code is a numerical representation of Health, Flammability and Reactivity hazards associated with the substance. Numbers range from 0 (low hazard) to 4 (extremely high hazard). OX indicates that the material is an oxidizer, and W̶ means the substance is water reactive.

Vapor Pressure. This is a relative ranking of how much vapor will be given off at room temperature. Vapor pressures will decrease and increase with temperature. It should be remembered that the strength of odor may not be an indication of vapor pressure since some substances have a greater odor than others when present at the same concentration.

Water Solubility. This is an indication of how soluble the substance is in water. A 0% water solubility indicates the substance is insoluble, while increasing percentages indicate increasing water solubilities. S. indicates the substance is completely water soluble. DEC. indicates the material decomposes when in the presence of water. If water is not listed as an incompatible material then this decomposition is not considered to be hazardous under most circumstances.

PPE. PPE (Proper Protective Equipment) is a listing of the level of protection that is recommended for a moderate size spill (30–50 gallons) as defined by 29 CFR 1910.1200. Adjustments may be needed if the spill is larger or smaller. Abbreviations are: BUT=butyl rubber; RUB=natural rubber; NEO=neoprene; NIT=nitrile rubber; POLY=polyethylene; VIN=polyvinyl alcohol; TEF=Teflon®; VIT=Viton®; and SAR=Saranex®. Recommendations followed by (+) indicate that available data suggest that this material will offer excellent resistance to the chemical. A (0) indicates the material may offer good protection to the chemical, and a (-) indicates that the material will offer poor protection.

Incompatibilities. This is a listing of those classes of chemical compounds that may react with the listed substance to produce a hazardous product (toxic or explosive) or may release large amounts of energy over a short period of time. This is not a comprehensive listing; rather it is a listing of representative incompatible materials. Definitions and explanations of terms used may be found at the back of this book.

SPILL. Recommended procedures that should be used to clean up spills are given. These are coded and explained in the back of this book. Recommended procedures may need to be modified according to circumstances.

DECON. These are recommended solutions that should be used to decontaminate spill areas. The following indicate which solutions should be used: BASE = dilute alkaline solution; ACID = dilute acid solution; SOAP = dilute soap solution; FLOOD. WATER = flooding quantities of water. DRY indicates that dry decontamination techniques should be used.

FIRE. This section contains codes that indicate recommended fire fighting agents and methods that should be used to extinguish fires involving the chemical. Methods may need to be altered according to circumstances present. Codes are explained in the back of this book.

FIRST AID. This section contains codes indicating those health issues that may be important to first responders. Codes are explained in the back of this book.

SPECIAL. These codes are explained in the back of this book and are present to bring some important issues associated with the chemical to the attention of the first responder.

The second section of this book contains isolation distances and reporting information. Individual sections are:

DOT ISOLATION. Distances given are those recommended by the US DOT from DOT publication P 5800.5. These distances are circular isolation distances that should be used when a chemical spill occurs and no fire is involved. The upper number is the distance to be used for a small spill (i.e., smaller than 55 gallons), while the lower number is for larger spills.

DOT TAKE COVER. Distances given are those recommended by the US DOT from DOT publication P 5800.5. These distances are downwind isolation distances that should be used when a chemical spill occurs and no fire is involved. The upper number is the distance to be used for a small spill (i.e., less than 55 gallons), while the upper number is for larger spills.

RCRA WASTE NUMBER. RCRA waste numbers from 40 CFR 302.4 are listed.

REPORTABLE QUANTITIES. Reportable quantities for potential wastes are given as per 40 CFR 302.4. The upper number is the "Final Reportable Quantity," and the lower number is the "Statutory Reportable Quantity."

SECTION ONE

GENERAL CHEMICAL INFORMATION

CHEMICAL NAME	DOT #	CAS #	FORM	NFPA	VAPOR PRESS.	WATER SOL.
ACETAL ***	1088	105-57-7	C. LIQ. < 1	2-3-0	MOD.	5%
ACETALDEHYDE	1089	75-07-0	C. LIQ. < 1	2-4-2	HIGH	S.
ACETALDEHYDE OXIME	2332	107-29-9	C. SOL.	---	LOW	S.
ACETIC ACID ***	2789 2790	64-19-7	C. LIQ. > 1	2-2-1	MOD.	S.
ACETIC ANHYDRIDE ***	1715	108-24-7	C. LIQ. > 1	2-2-1- W	LOW	DEC.
ACETOIN	2621	513-86-0	C. LIQ. < 1	---	---	S.
ACETONE ***	1090 1091	67-64-1	C. LIQ. < 1	1-3-0	HIGH	S.
ACETONE CYANOHYDRIN ***	1541	75-86-5	C. LIQ. < 1	4-1-2	LOW	S.
ACETONITRILE ***	1648	75-05-8	C. LIQ. < 1	3-3-0	HIGH	S.
ACETOZONE	2081	644-31-5	C. SOL. ---	---	LOW	DEC.
ACETYL BROMIDE ***	1716	506-96-7	FUM. LIQ. > 1	---	HIGH	DEC.
ACETYL CHLORIDE ***	1717	75-36-5	FUM. LIQ. > 1	3-3-2 W	HIGH	DEC.
ACETYLACETONE	2310	123-54-6	C. LIQ. < 1	2-2-0	---	12%
ACETYLENE	1001	74-86-2	C. GAS	1-4-3	GAS	0%

PPE	INCOMPATIBILITIES	SPILL	DECON.	FIRE	FIRST AID	SPECIAL
LEVEL B BUT(-)	OXIDIZERS	S1,S6	SOAP	F2,F7	H9	E1,E3,E4,E5
LEVEL B BUT(+)	ANHYDRIDES, P, NH₃ CYANIDES, OXIDIZERS, KETONES	S1,S7, S8	WATER	F2,F7	H1,H5, H6,H9	E1,E3,E4,E5, E6E16
LEVEL B ---	ACIDS, OXIDIZERS	S1	WATER	F2,F7	H9	E1,E7,E9
LEVEL B BUT(+) TEF(+) SAR(+)	OXIDIZERS	S1,S6	BASE	F1,F7, F8	H6,H7, H8,H9	E1,E3
LEVEL A BUT(0) TEF(0)	WATER, OLEUM AMINES, ALCOHOLS, OXIDIZERS	S1	BASE	F3,F7, F8,F9, F14	H6,H7, H8,H9	E1,E3,E12
LEVEL B ---	OXIDIZERS	S1,S6	WATER	F1,F7	H9	E1,E3
LEVEL B BUT(+) TEF(+)	OXIDIZERS, HALOFORMS, NITRIC ACID	S1,S6, S8	WATER	F2,F7	H9	E1,E3
LEVEL A BUT(-) TEF(-)	ACIDS, ALKALI, OXIDIZERS	S1,S7, S8	ALK. HYPO-CHLOR.	F2,F7, F9	H9,H10	E2,E7
LEVEL A BUT(+) TEF(+)	FLUORINE, NITRIC ACID, OXIDIZERS	S1,S6, S7,S8	WATER	F2,F7, F9	H9,H10	E2,E3,E7
LEVEL B BUT(-)	WATER, REDUCING AGENTS	S5	WATER	F1,F7 F10, F14	H6,H7, H8,H9	E1,E7,E8
LEVEL A TEF(0)	WATER, ALCOHOLS, AMINES, ALKALI, OXIDIZERS	S1,S6, S7	WATER	F3,F7, F8,F9	H6,H7, H8,H9	E1,E3,E7
LEVEL A TEF(0)	WATER, ALCOHOLS, AMINES, ALKALI OXIDIZERS	S1,S6, S7,S8	WATER	F3, F8,F9	H6,H7, H8,H9	E1,E3,E7, E9
LEVEL B ---	OXIDIZERS	S1,S6	WATER	F1,F7	H9	E1,E3,E5
LEVEL B ---	PRESSURE, Cu,Hg,NaH, OXIDIZERS, SILVER SALTS	S2,S5, S6	---	F1,F7	H11	E1,E3,E4, E6,E8,E10, E16

CHEMICAL NAME	DOT #	CAS #	FORM	NFPA	VAPOR PRESS.	WATER SOL.
ACETYLENE TETRABROMIDE	2504	79-27-6	YELL. LIQ. > 1	3-0-1	LOW	< 1%
ACRIDINE	2713	260-94-6	WHITE POWD.	---	LOW	NONE
ACROLEIN ***	1092	107-02-8	C. LIQ. < 1	3-3-3	HIGH	S.
ACRYLAMIDE ***	2074	79-06-1	WHITE POWD.	---	LOW	S.
ACRYLIC ACID ***	2218	79-10-7	C. LIQ. > 1	3-2-2	LOW	S.
ACRYLONITRILE ***	1093	107-13-1	C. LIQ < 1	4-3-2	HIGH	7%
ADIPONITRILE	2205	111-69-3	WHITE LIQ. < 1	4-2-1	LOW	S.
ALDOL	2839	107-89-1	C. LIQ. > 1	3-2-2	---	S.
ALDRIN® ***	2761	309-00-2	C. SOL. > 1	---	LOW	0%
ALLYL ACETATE	2833	591-87-7	C. LIQ. < 1	1-3-0	---	0%
ALLYL ALCOHOL ***	1098	107-18-6	C. LIQ. < 1	3-3-1	MOD.	S.
ALLYLAMINE ***	2334	107-11-9	C. LIQ. < 1	3-3-1	---	S.
ALLYL CHLORIDE ***	1100	107-05-1	C. LIQ. < 1	3-3-1	HIGH	0%
ALLYL CHLOROCARBONATE ***	1722	2937-50-2	C. LIQ. > 1	3-3-1	MOD.	DEC.

PPE	INCOMPATIBILITIES	SPILL	DECON.	FIRE	FIRST AID	SPECIAL
LEVEL B VIT(-)	ALKALI METALS, STRONG ALKALI, N_2O_4, OXIDIZERS	S3	SOAP	F6,F9	H1,H9	E1,E7,E9
LEVEL B BUT(-) VIT(-)	OXIDIZERS	S3,S7	SOAP	F6,F9	H1,H9	E1,E9
LEVEL A BUT(+)	ACIDS, ALKALI, NH_3, AMINES, OXIDIZERS	S1,S6, S7,S8	WATER	F2,F7	H6,H7, H8H9	E1,E3,E4, E5,E6
LEVEL A POLY(0) BUT(-)	OXIDIZERS	S3,S7, S8	WATER	F1,F9, F10, F11	H2,H9	E1,E9
LEVEL A BUT(+) SAR(+)	ACIDS, ALKALI, PEROXIDES, OXIDIZERS	S1,S7, S8	WATER	F2,F9, F10, F11	H1,H6, H7,H8, H9	E1,E3,E6
LEVEL A BUT(0)	HALOGENS, ACIDS, BASES, OXIDIZERS, PEROXIDES, AMINES	S1,S6, S7,S8	ALK. HYPO- CHLOR.	F2,F9 F7,F10	H1,H6, H7,H8, H9,H10	E2,E3,E4,E6, E9,E16
LEVEL A TEF(0) BUT(-)	ACIDS, OXIDIZERS	S1,S7	ALK. HYPO- CHLOR.	F1,F7, F9	H9,H10	E2,E7,E9
LEVEL A BUT(0)	OXIDIZERS	S1,S7	WATER	F2,F7, F9	H9	E1,E3,
LEVEL A ---	ACIDS, OXIDIZERS, PHENOL	S3,S7, S8	SOAP	F1,F7 F9	H1,H9	E2,E9,E10
LEVEL B ---	PEROXIDES, OXIDIZERS	S1,S7	SOAP	F1,F7	H9	E1,E3, E6
LEVEL A BUT(+) TEF(+) VIT(0)	ACIDS, PEROXIDES, CARBON TETRACHLORIDE, OXIDIZERS	S1,S6, S7,S8	WATER	F2,F7, F9	H6,H7, H8,H9	E1,E3, E6
LEVEL A BUT (-)	ACIDS, HALOGENS, HALOCARBONS, OXIDIZERS	S1,S6, S7	WATER	F2,F7, F9	H6,H7, H8,H9	E2,E3,E4, E9
LEVEL A TEF(+) VIN (-)	Zn, Al, Mg, BF_3, $AlCl_3$, ACIDS, AMINES, OXIDIZERS	S1,S6, S7	SOAP	F1,F7, F9,F10	H1,H6, H7,H8, H9	E1,E3,E6,E9
LEVEL A ---	ACIDS, AMINES, ALCOHOL, WATER, RUST, OXIDIZERS	S1,S6, S7	WATER	F1,F7, F8,F9, F10	H6,H7, H8,H9	E2,E3,E7,E9

CHEMICAL NAME	DOT #	CAS #	FORM	NFPA	VAPOR PRESS.	WATER SOL.
ALLYL GLYCIDYL ETHER	2219	106-92-3	C. LIQ. < 1	---	LOW	0%
ALLYL ISOTHIOCYANATE	1545	57-06-7	C. LIQ. > 1	3-2-0	LOW	1%
ALLYL TRICHLOROSILANE	1724	107-37-9	C. LIQ. > 1	3-3-2- W	MOD.	DEC.
ALUMINUM (POWDERED)	1309, 1383, 1396	7429-90-5	GREY-WHITE POWD.	0-1-1	NONE	0%
ALUMINUM CHLORIDE (ANHYDROUS)	1726	7446-70-0	WHITE, FUME SOL.	---	NONE	S.
ALUMINUM NITRATE	1438	7784-27-2 13473-90-0	WHITE POWD.	---	LOW	64%
ALUMINUM PHOSPHIDE ***	1397	20859-73-8	GREY POWD.	3-4-2 W	LOW	DEC.
AMINOETHOXY-ETHANOL	1760	929-06-6	C. LIQ. > 1	---	---	S.
AMINOETHYL-PIPERAZINE	2815	140-31-8	C. LIQ. 1.0	2-2-0	---	S.
p-AMINOPHENOL	2512	123-30-8	WHITE POWD.	---	---	< 1%
AMINOPROPYL-DIETHANOLAMINE	1760	123-00-2	C. LIQ. 1.0	2-1-0	LOW	S.
2-AMINOPYRIDINE	2671	504-29-0	WHITE POWD.	---	---	S.
AMMONIA ***	1005	7664-91-7	GAS	3-1-0	GAS	S.
AMMONIUM ARSENATE	1546	7784-44-3	WHITE POWD.	---	---	S.

PPE	INCOMPATIBILITIES	SPILL	DECON.	FIRE	FIRST AID	SPECIAL
LEVEL B ---	OXIDIZERS	S1,S7	SOAP	F1,F7	H6,H7, H8,H9	E1,E3,E5
LEVEL A ---	WATER, ALCOHOL, AMINES, HEAT, OXIDIZERS	S1,S6, S7	SOAP	F1,F7, F9,F10	H1,H5, H6,H7, H8,H9	E2,E3,E6,E7, E9,E16
LEVEL B ---	WATER, ACIDS, ALKALI, OXIDIZERS	S1,S6, S7	WATER	F3,F7, F8,F9	H6,H7, H8,H9	E1,E3,E7,E9
LEVEL C ---	HALOCARBONS, S, Se, P, ACIDS, HALOGENS, ALCOHOLS, OXIDIZERS, ALKALI	S3	SOAP	F5,F7, F8,	H9	E1,E7,E11, E12
LEVEL B ---	WATER	S4	BASE	F3	H6,H7, H8,H9	E1,E7,E12
LEVEL B ---	POWDERED METALS, REDUCING AGENTS	S3	WATER	F4,F7	H9	E1,E9,E13
LEVEL A ---	WATER, ACID	S8,S9	---	F5,F12 F13	H6,H7, H8,H9	E2,E7
LEVEL B BUT(-) VIT(-)	ACIDS, OXIDIZERS	S1,S7	WATER	F1,F7	H6,H7, H8,H9	E1,E3,E5,E9
LEVEL B BUT(0)	OXIDIZERS	S1,S7	WATER	F1,F7	H6,H7, H8,H9	E1,E9
LEVEL B BUT(-) VIN(-)	OXIDIZERS	S3,S7	SOAP	F1,F7, F9	H5,H9, H12	E1,E9
LEVEL B ---	OXIDIZERS	S1,S7	WATER	F2,F7	H6,H7, H8,H9	E1,E9
LEVEL B ---	OXIDIZERS	S3,S7	WATER	F1,F7, F9	H9	E2,E7,E9
LEVEL B BUT(+) TEF(+)	HALOGENS, ACIDS, INTERHALOGENS, OXIDIZERS	S2,S5, S6	WATER	F6,F7, F9,F10	H6,H7, H8,H9, H13	E1,E3,E9,E16
LEVEL B RUB(-) NEO(-) NIT(-)	HALOGENS, OXIDIZERS	S3,S7	WATER	F6F7, F9	H2,H9	E1,E9

CHEMICAL NAME	DOT #	CAS #	FORM	NFPA	VAPOR PRESS.	WATER SOL.
AMMONIUM BIFLUORIDE ***	1727 2817	1341-49-7	WHITE POWD.	---	---	S.
AMMONIUM DICHROMATE	1439	7789-09-5	RED CRYST.	2-1-1 OX	---	S.
AMMONIUM FLUORIDE ***	2505	12125-01-8	WHITE POWD.	3-0-0	---	S.
AMMONIUM NITRATE	0222 1942 2426	6484-52-2	WHITE POWD.	1-0-3 OX	---	S.
AMMONIUM PERCHLORATE	0402 1442	7790-98-9	WHITE POWD.	1-0-4 OX	---	S.
AMMONIUM PERMANGANATE	9190	13446-10-1	PURP. POWD.	1-0-3 OX	---	S.
AMMONIUM PERSULFATE	1444	7727-54-0	WHITE POWD.	---	LOW	S.
AMMONIUM PICRATE ***	0004 1310	131-74-8	YELL. POWD.	---	LOW	1%
AMMONIUM VANADATE ***	2859	7803-55-6	WHITE POWD.	---	LOW	1%
AMYL ACETATE ***	1104	628-63-7	C. LIQ. < 1	1-3-0	MOD.	0.2%
AMYL ALCOHOL	1105	71-41-0	C. LIQ. < 1	1-3-0	MOD.	2%
AMYLALDEHYDE	2058	110-62-3	C. LIQ. < 1	1-3-0	---	0%
AMYLAMINE	1106	110-58-7	C. LIQ. < 1	3-3-0	---	S.
AMYLBUTYRATE	2620	540-18-1	C. LIQ. < 1	1-2-0	---	0%

PPE	INCOMPATIBILITIES	SPILL	DECON.	FIRE	FIRST AID	SPECIAL
LEVEL A BUT(-) SAR(-) NEO(-)	ACIDS, ALKALI, CALCIUM SALTS	S3,S7	BASE	F1,F7, F9	H8,H9	E2,E9
LEVEL B POLY(-) SAR(-)	ACIDS, ALCOHOLS, HYDRAZINE, REDUCING AGENTS	S3,S7	WATER	F4,F7, F10 F11	H2,H8, H9	E2,E7,E9, E13,E14,E16
LEVEL A NEO(0) NIT(0)	ALKALI	S3,S7	BASE	F6,F7, F9	H9	E2,E9
LEVEL B ---	COMBUSTIBLES, POWDERED METALS, UREA, S, SULFIDES	S3,S7	WATER	F4,F7, F9,F10 F11	H5,H9	E1,E9,E14
LEVEL B ---	COMBUSTIBLES, P, S, POWDERED METALS, Cl, ClO2, Al, Cu	S3	BISULF.	F4,F7, F11	H9	E1,E8,E13, E16
LEVEL C ---	COMBUSTIBLES, POWDERED METALS, REDUCING AGENTS	S3,S7	WATER	F4,F7, F11, F12	H6,H7, H8,H9	E1,E8,E13, E14,E16
LEVEL B ---	Fe,Ag,Al,Zn,NH3,ACIDS, POWDERED METALS, REDUCING AGENTS	S3,S7	BISULF.	F4,F7, F11, F12	H6,H7, H8,H9	E1,E8, E14,E16
LEVEL B ---	REDUCING AGENTS	S3,S7, S8	SOAP	F4,F7, F12	H5,H9	E1,E8,E14, E16
LEVEL B ---	---	S3,S7, S8	SOAP	F6,F7	H9	E1
LEVEL B VIN(0)	OXIDIZERS	S1,S7, S8	SOAP	F1,F7, F11	H9	E1,E3
LEVEL B BUT(+) TEF(+) VIT(0)	OXIDIZERS	S1,S6	WATER	F2,F7, F11, F12	H9	E1,E3
LEVEL B TEF(0) BUT(-)	OXIDIZERS	S1,S6, S7	SOAP	F2,F7, F11, F12	H9	E1,E3
LEVEL B TEF(-)	OXIDIZERS	S1,S6, S7	WATER	F2,F7, F11, F12	H6,H7, H8,H9	E1,E9,E3
LEVEL B ---	OXIDIZERS	S1,S6, S7	SOAP	F2,F7, F11, F12	H9	E1,E3

CHEMICAL NAME	DOT #	CAS #	FORM	NFPA	VAPOR PRESS.	WATER SOL.
AMYL CHLORIDE	1107	543-59-9	C. LIQ. < 1	1-3-0	---	0%
AMYLENE	1108	109-67-1	C. LIQ. < 1	1-4-0	HIGH	0%
AMYL FORMATE	1109	638-49-3	C. LIQ. < 1	1-3-0	---	0%
AMYL MERCAPTAN	1111	110-66-7	C. LIQ. < 1	2-3-0	MOD.	0%
AMYL NITRATE	1112	1002-16-0	C. LIQ. < 1	2-2-0 OX	---	0%
AMYL NITRITE	1113	463-04-7	C. LIQ. < 1	1-2-2	---	0%
ANILINE ***	1547	62-53-3	C. LIQ. > 1	3-2-0	LOW	4%
o-ANISIDINE	2431	90-04-0	RED LIQ. > 1	2-1-0	LOW	0%
ANISOLE	2222	100-66-3	C. LIQ. 1.0	1-2-0	HIGH	0%
p-ANISOLYL CHLORIDE	1729	100-07-2	C. LIQ. ---	---	---	0%
ANTIMONY ***	2871	7440-36-0	SILV. METAL	---	NONE	0%
ANTIMONY PENTACHLORIDE ***	1730 1731	7647-18-9	C. LIQ. > 1	3-0-1	LOW	DEC.
ANTIMONY TRICHLORIDE ***	1733	10025-91-9	CRYST.	---	MOD.	DEC.
ARSENIC ***	1558, 1561	7440-38-2	SILV. METAL	---	LOW	0%

PPE	INCOMPATIBILITIES	SPILL	DECON.	FIRE	FIRST AID	SPECIAL
LEVEL B TEF(-) VIT(-)	OXIDIZERS	S1,S6, S7	SOAP	F2,F7, F11, F12	H9	E1,E3,E7, E9
LEVEL B VIT(-)	OXIDIZERS,	S1,S6,S 7	SOAP	F2,F7, F11, F12	H9	E1,E3,E4,E5, E6
LEVEL B ---	OXIDIZERS,	S1,S6, S7	SOAP	F2,F7, F11, F12	H9	E1,E3
LEVEL B	OXIDIZERS	S1,S6, S7	SOAP	F2,F7, F11, F12	H9	E1,E3,E9
LEVEL B ---	OXIDIZERS, REDUCING AGENTS	S1,S6	SOAP	F2,F7, F11, F12	H9,H12	E1,E3,E14, E16
LEVEL B	OXIDIZERS, REDUCING AGENTS	S1,S6, S7	SOAP	F2,F7, F11, F12	H9	E1,E3,E14, E16
LEVEL A BUT(+) VIN(+) TEF(0) SAR(0)	OXIDIZERS, ALKALI, ACIDS	S1,S6, S7,S8	SOAP	F1,F7, F9,F11	H2,H6, H7,H8, H9,H12	E2,E3,E7, E9
LEVEL A ---	OXIDIZERS	S1,S7	SOAP	F1,F7, F9	H2,H5, H9	E1,E9
LEVEL B ---	OXIDIZERS	S1,S6, S7	SOAP	F2,F7, F11	H9	E1,E3
LEVEL A ---	WATER	S1,S7	BASE	F1,F7, F9	H6,H7, H8,H9	E1,E7,E9,E15
LEVEL B ---	H2, HALOGENS, OXIDIZERS	S3	SOAP	F6	H9	E1,E7
LEVEL A ---	WATER	S3,S7	BASE	F6,F7, F8	H6,H7, H8,H9	E1,E7
LEVEL A ---	Al, WATER, ALKALI METALS	S3,S6,S 7	BASE	F6,F7, F8	H6,H7, H8,H9	E1,E7
LEVEL A ---	HALOGENS, H2, Pb, Zn, Pt, ALKALI METALS, OXIDIZERS	S3,S7	SOAP	F6,F7, F9	H2,H9	E2,E7,E9

CHEMICAL NAME	DOT #	CAS #	FORM	NFPA	VAPOR PRESS.	WATER SOL.
ARSENIC ACID ***	1553 1554	7778-39-4	WHITE CRYST.	---	---	S.
ARSENIC TRISULFIDE ***	1557	1303-33-9	RED SOL.	---	---	0%
ARSENIC TRICHLORIDE ***	1560	7784-34-1	C. LIQ. > 1	3-0-0	MOD.	DEC.
ARSENIC TRIOXIDE ***	1561	1327-53-3	WHITE POWD.	2-0-0	LOW	0%
ARSINE ***	2188	7784-42-1	C. GAS	4-4-2	GAS	20%
BARIUM	1399 1400 1854	7440-39-3	WHITE SOL.	---	---	DEC.
BARIUM BROMATE	2719	13967-90-3	WHITE POWD.	2-0-1 OX	LOW	S.
BARIUM CYANIDE ***	1565	542-62-1	WHITE POWD.	---	LOW	S.
BARIUM NITRATE	1446	10022-31-8	WHITE POWD.	---	LOW	S.
BARIUM OXIDE	1884	1304-28-5	WHITE POWD.	---	LOW	DEC.
BARIUM PEROXIDE	1449	1304-29-6	WHITE POWD.	---	---	<1%
BENZALDEHYDE	1989	100-52-7	C. LIQ. > 1	2-2-0	LOW	<1%
BENZENE ***	1114	71-43-2	C. LIQ. < 1	2-3-0	HIGH	0%
BENZENE SULFONYL CHLORIDE ***	2225	98-09-9	C. LIQ. > 1	---	LOW	DEC.

PPE	INCOMPATIBILITIES	SPILL	DECON.	FIRE	FIRST AID	SPECIAL
LEVEL A ---	REDUCING AGENTS	S3,S7, S8	WATER	F6,F7, F9	H2,H9	E2,E9
LEVEL A ---	ACIDS, OXIDIZERS, WATER	S3,S7	SOAP	F6,F7, F9	H2,H9	E2,E7,E9
LEVEL A	Al, WATER	S3,S6, S7	BASE	F6,F7, F9	H2,H8, H9	E2,E7, E9
LEVEL A ---	ACIDS, HALOGENS, Al,Zn,Hg,OXIDIZERS, INTERHALOGENS	S3,S7, S8	SOAP	F6,F7, F9	H1,H9	E2,E7,E9
LEVEL A ---	ACIDS, LIGHT, HALOGENS, OXIDIZERS	S2,S5, S6	---	F1,F7, F9,F11 F12	H2,H9	E2,E3,E7, E9
LEVEL B ---	WATER, ACIDS, HALOGENS,OXIDIZERS	S3,S7	FLOOD WATER	F5,F7, F12, F13, F15	H8,H9	E1,E7,E9, E16
LEVEL B ---	NH3,C, Cu,Al,METAL SULFIDES, HEAT, COMBUSTIBLES	S3,S7	WATER	F4,F11 F12	H8,H9	E2,E9,E13, E14
LEVEL A ---	ACIDS, OXIDIZERS	S3,S7, S8	ALK. HYPO-CHLOR.	F1,F7, F9	H9,H10	E2,E7,E9
LEVEL B	Mg,Al,Zn,B,CYANIDES, AMINES, Hg SALTS, COMBUSTIBLES REDUCING AGENTS	S3,S11	WATER	F4,F11 F12	H9	E1,E13,E14
LEVEL B ---	ACIDS,WATER, COMBUSTIBLES, REDUCING AGENTS	S3	BASE	F6	H6,H7, H8,H9	E1,E7,E12
LEVEL B ---	Al,Mg,COMBUSTIBLES, H2S, REDUCING AGENTS, WATER	S10, S11	FLOOD WATER	F4,F11 F12	H8,H9	E1,E7,E14, E16
LEVEL B DUT(1) VIT(0)	OXIDIZERS	S1,S6, S7	SOAP	F2,F7 F9	H1,H9	E1,E3
LEVEL A VIN(1) TEF(0)	OXIDIZERS, FLUORIDES	S1,S7, S8	SOAP	F2,F7	H2,H9	E1,E3,E9
LEVEL B VIN(-) VIT(-)	DIMETHYL SULFOXIDE, METHYL FORMAMIDE, WATER	S1,S7, S8	BASE	F1,F7, F9	H6,H7, H8,H9	E1,E7,E12

CHEMICAL NAME	DOT #	CAS #	FORM	NFPA	VAPOR PRESS.	WATER SOL.
BENZIDINE ***	1885	92-87-5	WHITE CRYST.	---	LOW	< 1%
BENZOYL PEROXIDE	2085 2086 2087 2088 2089 2090	94-36-0	WHITE POWD.	---	---	0%
BENZONITRILE ***	2224	100-47-0	C. LIQ. > 1	---	LOW	1%
BENZOQUINONE ***	2587	106-51-4	WHITE SOL.	1-2-1	LOW	0%
BENZOTRICHLORIDE ***	2226	98-07-7	FUM. LIQ. > 1	3-1-0	LOW	0%
BENZOTRIFLUORIDE	2338	98-08-8	C. LIQ. > 1	4-3-0	MOD.	0%
BENZOYL CHLORIDE ***	1736	98-88-4	C. LIQ. > 1	3-2-2 W	LOW	DEC.
BENZYL BROMIDE	1737	100-39-0	C. LIQ. > 1	---	LOW	0%
BENZYL CHLORIDE ***	1738	100-44-7	C. LIQ. > 1	2-2-1	LOW	0%
BERYLLIUM ***	1567	7440-41-7	GREY METAL	3-1-0	LOW	0%
BERYLLIUM FLUORIDE ***	1566	7787-49-7	WHITE CRYST.	---	LOW	S
BERYLLIUM NITRATE ***	2464	13597-99-4	WHITE CRYST.	---	---	S
BIS (CHLOROMETHYL) ETHER ***	2249	542-88-1	C. LIQ. > 1	---	---	DEC.

PPE	INCOMPATIBILITIES	SPILL	DECON.	FIRE	FIRST AID	SPECIAL
LEVEL A ---	OXIDIZERS, NITRIC ACID	S3,S7, S8	SOAP	F6,F7, F9	H2,H9	E1,E9
LEVEL B ---	REDUCING AGENTS, COMBUSTIBLES, AMINES	S9	FLOOD WATER	F1,F7, F10 F12	H1,H9	E1,E8,E9, E14,E16
LEVEL B BUT(+) VIN(+)	ACIDS, ALKALI, OXIDIZERS	S1,S7	SOAP	F1,F7, F9	H9,H10	E1,E7,E9
LEVEL B SAR(+)	OXIDIZERS	S3,S7, S8	SOAP	F1,F7, F9	H8,H9	E1,E9
LEVEL A ---	OXIDIZERS	S1,S7, S8	SOAP	F2,F7, F9	H6,H7, H8,H9	E2,E9
LEVEL A ---	WATER, OXIDIZERS	S1,S6, S7	BASE	F1,F7, F9,F12	H6,H7, H8,H9	E2,E7,E9
LEVEL B VIN(+) VIT(0)	WATER, OXIDIZERS, AlCl3, DIMETHYL SULFOXIDE	S2,S3, S6,S7	BASE	F3,F7, F9,F14	H6,H7, H8,H9	E2,E7,E9, E12
LEVEL A TEF(-)	OXIDIZERS	S3,S7	SOAP	F1,F7, F9	H6,H7, H8,H9	E2,E9
LEVEL A TEF(0)	WATER, HEAT, METALS	S1,S7, S8,S11	SOAP	F1,F7, F9,F10	H1,H6, H7, H8,H9	E2,E7,E7, E9,E14
LEVEL A ---	ACIDS,BASES,Li,P, HALOCARBONS, HALOGENS	S3,S7, S8	SOAP	F1,F7, F9	H2,H6, H7,H9	E2,E9
LEVEL A ---	ACIDS,Mg	S3,S7	WATER	F6,F7, F9	H2,H9	E2,E7,E9
LEVEL A ---	COMBUSTIBLES, REDUCING AGENTS	S3,S7	WATER	F4,F7, F9,F12	H2,H6, H7,H9	E2,E9,E13
LEVEL A TEF(-)	ACIDS, WATER	S1,S6, S7,S8	BASE	F1,F7, F9	H1,H6, H9	E2,E5,E7, E9,E12

CHEMICAL NAME	DOT #	CAS #	FORM	NFPA	VAPOR PRESS.	WATER SOL.
*** 1,1-BIS (4-CHLOROPHENYL)- 2,2- DICHLOROETHANE	2761	72-54-8	C. LIQ. ---	---	LOW	0%
BORNEOL	1312	507-70-0	WHITE POWD.	2-2-0	---	0%
BORON TRIBROMIDE ***	2692	10294-33-4	C. LIQ. > 1	4-0-2 ~~W~~	HIGH	DEC.
BORON TRICHLORIDE ***	1741	10294-34-5	C. LIQ. > 1	---	GAS	DEC.
BORON TRIFLUORIDE ***	1009	7637-07-2	FUM. GAS	4-0-1	GAS	DEC.
BROMINE ***	1744	7726-95-6	RED LIQ. > 1	3-0-0 OX	HIGH	16%
BROMINE PENTAFLUORIDE ***	1745	7789-30-2	FUM. LIQ. > 1	4-0-3 ~~W~~-OX	---	DEC.
BROMINE TRIFLUORIDE ***	1746	7787-71-5	FUM. LIQ. > 1	4-0-3 ~~W~~-OX	---	DEC.
BROMOACETIC ACID	1938	79-08-3	CRYST.	---	---	S.
BROMOACETONE ***	1569	598-31-2	C. LIQ. > 1	---	---	< 1%
BROMOBENZENE	2514	108-86-1	C. LIQ. > 1	2-2-0	MOD.	0%
1-BROMOBUTANE	1126	109-65-9	C. LIQ. > 1	2-3-0	MOD.	0%
2-BROMOBUTANE	2339	78-76-2	C. LIQ. > 1	---	---	0%
BROMOFORM ***	2515	75-25-2	C. LIQ. > 1	---	---	0%

PPE	INCOMPATIBILITIES	SPILL	DECON.	FIRE	FIRST AID	SPECIAL
LEVEL B ---	OXIDIZERS	S3,S7, S8	SOAP	F1,F7, F9	H2,H9	E1,E9
LEVEL A ---	OXIDIZERS	S1,S7	SOAP	F1,F7 F12	H9	E1,E9
LEVEL A ---	WATER, ALCOHOLS, ALKALI METALS, TUNGSTEN TRIOXIDE	S3,S6, S7	BASE	F5,F7, F9, F14	H6,H7, H8,H9	E2,E7,E10, E12
LEVEL A ---	WATER, COMBUSTIBLES	S5,S6	---	F5,F8, F9,F10 F11, F14	H6,H7, H8,H9	E2,E7,E9, E10,E12
LEVEL A ---	WATER, ALKALI METALS, COMBUSTIBLES	S5,S6	---	F5,F8, F10, F11, F14	H6,H7, H8,H9	E2,E7,E10, E12
LEVEL A TEF(0)	COMBUSTIBLES,AZIDES, METALS, H2,NH3 REDUCING AGENTS	S3,S6, S7	WATER	F6,F7, F9	H6,H7, H8,H9	E2,E7,E9
LEVEL A ---	WATER,NH3,METALS, HALOGENS,P, AMMONIA SALTS	S3,S6, S7	FLOOD WATER	F5,F8, F9,F10	H6,H7, H8,H9	E2,E7,E9, E12,E16
LEVEL A ---	WATER,ACIDS,BASES, METALS,HALOGENS	S3,S6, S7	FLOOD WATER	F3,F8, F9	H6,H7, H8,H9	E2,E7,E9, E12,E16
LEVEL B ---	OXIDIZERS, BASES	S3	WATER	F1,F7, F9	H6,H7, H8,H9	E1,E9
LEVEL A ---	OXIDIZERS	S3,S7, S8	SOAP	F1,F7, F9	H9	E1,E9
LEVEL B VIN(+) VIT(+)	ALKALI METALS, OXIDIZERS	S1,S6, S7	SOAP	F1,F7, F9,F11	H9	E1,E3,E9
LEVEL B NIT(-) VIT(-)	ALKALI METALS, OXIDIZERS	S1,S6, S7	SOAP	F1,F7, F9	H9	E1,E3,E9
LEVEL B NIT(-) VIT(-)	ALKALI METALS, Mg, OXIDIZERS	S1,S7	SOAP	F1,F7, F9	H9	E1,E3,E9
LEVEL B VIT(-)	ALKALI METALS, Zn, BASES, ETHERS, ACETONE	S1,S7, S8	SOAP	F6,F9, F11	H1,H9	E1,E3,E9

CHEMICAL NAME	DOT #	CAS #	FORM	NFPA	VAPOR PRESS.	WATER SOL.
2-BROMOPENTANE	2343	107-81-3	C. LIQ. > 1	1-3-0	---	0%
1-BROMOPROPANE	2344	106-94-5	C. LIQ. > 1	2-3-0	HIGH	0%
3-BROMOPROPYNE	2345	106-96-7	C. LIQ. > 1	4-3-4	---	0%
BRUCINE ***	1570	5892-11-5	WHITE POWD.	---	NONE	< 1%
1,3-BUTADIENE	1010	106-99-0	C. GAS	2-4-2	GAS	0%
BUTANE	1011, 1075	106-97-8	C. GAS	1-4-0	GAS	0%
1-BUTANOL ***	1120	71-36-3	C. LIQ. < 1	1-3-0	---	9%
n-BUTYL ACETATE ***	1123	122-86-4	C. LIQ. < 1	1-3-0	MOD.	0%
n-BUTYL ACRYLATE	2348	141-32-3	C. LIQ. < 1	2-2-2	LOW	0%
n-BUTYLAMINE ***	1125	109-73-9	C. LIQ. < 1	3-3-0	HIGH	S
n-BUTYL ALDEHYDE	1129	123-72-8	C. LIQ. < 1	2-3-2	HIGH	S
n-BUTYL BENZENE	2709	104-51-8	C. LIQ. < 1	2-2-0	LOW	0%
n-BUTYL CHLORIDE	1127	109-69-3	C. LIQ. < 1	2-3-0	HIGH	0%
BUTYL ETHER	1149	142-96-1	C. LIQ. < 1	2-3-1	---	0%

PPE	INCOMPATIBILITIES	SPILL	DECON.	FIRE	FIRST AID	SPECIAL
LEVEL B ---	OXIDIZERS	S1,S7	SOAP	F1,F7, F9	H9	E1,E3,E9
LEVEL B ---	OXIDIZERS	S1,S6, S7	SOAP	F1,F7, F9	H9	E1,E3,E9
LEVEL A ---	Cu,Hg,Ag, OXIDIZERS,HEAT, PRESSURE	S1,S6	SOAP	F1,F7, F9	H9	E2,E3,E8,E9, E10,E16
LEVEL B ---	OXIDIZERS	S3,S7, S8	SOAP	F1,F7, F9	H9	E2,E9
LEVEL B BUT(+) VIT(+)	HALOGENS,O₂,Cu, Cu ALLOYS OXIDIZERS	S5,S6	---	F1,F7, F9,F10	H2,H9	E1,E3,E4,E5, E6,E8,E16
LEVEL B VIT(-)	OXIDIZERS	S5,S6	---	F1,F7	H9,H13	E1,E3
LEVEL B TEF(+) BUT(0) POLY(0)	Cu and ALLOYS, ANHYDRIDES OXIDIZERS	S1,S7, S8	WATER	F2,F7	H9	E1,E3
LEVEL B TEF(0) VIN(0)	OXIDIZERS	S1,S6	SOAP	F2,F7	H9	E1,E3
LEVEL B TEF(0)	OXIDIZERS	S1,S7	SOAP	F1,F7	H9	E1,E3,E5, E6
LEVEL A TEF(0)	OXIDIZERS, Cu, Al, HALOGENS	S1,S6, S7	WATER	F2,F7, F9	H6,H7, H8,H9	E1,E3,E9
LEVEL B BUT(+) TEF(+)	OXIDIZERS, ACIDS	S1,S6, S7	WATER	F2,F7, F9	H6,H7, H8,H9	E1,E3,E9
LEVEL B ---	OXIDIZERS	S1,S7	SOAP	F1,F7	H9	E1,E3
LEVEL B VIN(+)	OXIDIZERS	S1S6, S7	SOAP	F1,F7, F9	H9	E1,E3,E4,E9
LEVEL B TEF(-)	OXIDIZERS	S1	SOAP	F1,F7	H9	E1,E3,E5

CHEMICAL NAME	DOT #	CAS #	FORM	NFPA	VAPOR PRESS.	WATER SOL.
n-BUTYL ISOCYANATE ***	2485	111-36-4	C. LIQ. < 1	3-2-2	MOD.	DEC.
BUTYRIC ACID ***	2820	107-92-6	C. LIQ. < 1	3-2-0	LOW	S.
BUTYRIC ANHYDRIDE	2739	106-31-0	C. LIQ. < 1	1-2-1 W	---	DEC.
CACODYLIC ACID ***	1572	75-60-5	WHITE POWD.	---	NONE	S.
CADMIUM CHLORIDE ***	2570	10108-64-2	WHITE POWD. > 1	---	NONE	S.
CALCIUM CARBIDE ***	1402	75-20-7	GREY POWD. > 1	1-3-2 W	NONE	DEC.
CALCIUM CHLORATE	1452 2429	10137-74-3	WHITE POWD.	1-0-1 OX	---	S.
CALCIUM CHLORITE	1453	14674-72-7	WHITE POWD.	---	NONE	S.
CALCIUM CYANIDE ***	1575	592-01-8	WHITE POWD.	3-0-1	NONE	S.
CALCIUM HYDRIDE	1404	7789-78-8	GREY POWD.	---	NONE	DEC.
CALCIUM HYPOCHLORITE	1748 2208 2880	7778-54-3	WHITE POWD.	1-0-2 OX	NONE	DEC.
CALCIUM OXIDE	1910	1305-78-8	WHITE POWD.	---	NONE	DEC.
CALCIUM PERMANGANATE	1456	10118-76-0	PURP. POWD.	---	NONE	S.
CALCIUM PEROXIDE	1457	1305-79-9	WHITE POWD.	---	NONE	DEC.
CALCIUM PHOSPHIDE	1360	1305-99-3	RED POWD.	---	NONE	DEC.

PPE	INCOMPATIBILITIES	SPILL	DECON.	FIRE	FIRST AID	SPECIAL
LEVEL A ---	WATER,AMINES, ALCOHOLS, ACIDS	S1,S6, S7	BASE	F3,F7, F9	H6,H7, H8,H9	E2,E3,E7,E9
LEVEL B BUT(+) VIT(+)	OXIDIZERS	S1,S7	WATER	F2,F7, F9	H6,H7, H8,H9	E1,E3,E9
LEVEL B ---	OXIDIZERS, WATER	S1	BASE	F1,F7, F8,F9	H6,H7, H8,H9	E1,E3,E9,E12
LEVEL B ---	OXIDIZERS	S1,S7, S8	ACID	F1,F7, F9	H1,H9	E2,E9
LEVEL B ---	ALKALI METALS	S3,S7	WATER	F6,F7, F9	H2,H9	E1,E9
LEVEL B ---	WATER, HALOGENS, OXIDIZERS, HALOCARBONS	S2,S3, S6	FLOOD WATER	F5,F7, F8, F13	H6,H7, H8,H9	E2,E7,E12, E16
LEVEL B ---	S,Cu,As,Al,P,SULFIDES, COMBUSTIBLES, ACIDS	S3,S7	WATER	F4,F7, F9	H9	E1,E7,E12
LEVEL A ---	COMBUSTIBLES, THIOCYANATES	S3	WATER	F4,F7, F9	H9	E1,E7,E9
LEVEL B TEF(-)	ACIDS, OXIDIZERS	S3,S6, S7,S8	ALK. HYPO- CHLOR.	F6,F7, F9, F15	H9,H10	E2,E7,E9
LEVEL B ---	ACIDS, HALOGENS, ALCOHOLS, WATER, OXIDIZERS	S2,S3, S6.S7	FLOOD WATER	F5,F7, F12 F13	H6,H7, H8,H9	E1,E7,E14, E16
LEVEL A VIN(-) RUB(-) NEO(-)	ACIDS,COMBUSTIBLES, ALCOHOLS, HEAT	S1,S7	WATER	F4,F7, F9	H6,H7, H8,H9	E1,E7,E9, E13,E14
LEVEL B NIT(-) NEO(-)	ACIDS, HALOGENS, ALCOHOLS, P_2O_5	S3	ACID	F4,F7, F9	H6,H7, H8,H9	E1,E9,E12
LEVEL B ---	COMBUSTIBLES	S3,S7	WATER	F4,F7, F9	H9	E1,E9
LEVEL B ---	WATER, COMBUSTIBLES	S3,S7	FLOOD. WATER	F4,F7, F9	H9	E1,E7,E9, E13,E16
LEVEL A ---	WATER, ClO_2	S9	---	F5,F7, F8F9, F13	H8,H9	E2,E7,E9, E16

CHEMICAL NAME	DOT #	CAS #	FORM	NFPA	VAPOR PRESS.	WATER SOL.
CAMPHENE	9011	79-92-5	CRYST.	---	LOW	0%
CAMPHOR	2717	76-22-2	CRYST.	---	LOW	0%
CAMPHOR OIL	1130	8008-51-3	YELL. LIQ. < 1	< 1	---	0%
CAPROIC ACID	1760 2829	142-62-1	C. LIQ. < 1	2-1-0	LOW	1%
CARBARYL ***	2757	63-25-2	WHITE POWD.	---	NONE	< 1%
CARBOFURAN ***	2757	1563-66-2	WHITE POWD.	---	NONE	< 1%
CARBON DIOXIDE	1013 1845 2187	124-38-4	GAS	---	GAS	S.
CARBON DISULFIDE ***	1131	75-15-0	C. LIQ. < 1	2-3-0	HIGH	0%
CARBON MONOXIDE ***	1016 9202	630-08-0	GAS	2-4-0	GAS	2%
CARBON TETRABROMIDE	2516	558-13-4	WHITE SOL.	---	---	0%
CARBON TETRACHLORIDE ***	1846	56-23-5	C. LIQ. > 1	3-0-0	HIGH	0%
CARBONYL FLUORIDE ***	2417	353-50-4	C. GAS	---	GAS	DEC.
CARBONYL SULFIDE ***	2204	463-58-1	C. GAS	3-4-1	GAS	S.
CERIUM	1333 3078	7440-45-1	GREY SOL.	---	NONE	DEC.

PPE	INCOMPATIBILITIES	SPILL	DECON.	FIRE	FIRST AID	SPECIAL
LEVEL B ---	OXIDIZERS	S1	SOAP	F1,F7	H9	E1
LEVEL A ---	OXIDIZERS, HALOCARBONS	S1,S7	SOAP	F1,F7	H8,H9	E1
LEVEL B ---	OXIDIZERS	S1,S7	SOAP	F1,F7	H9	E1,E3
LEVEL B VIT(-) SAR(-)	OXIDIZERS	S3	SOAP	F1,F7	H8,H9	E1
LEVEL A NIT(0) NEO(0) VIN(0)	OXIDIZERS	S3,S7	SOAP	F1,F7, F9	H9	E2,E9
LEVEL A ---	ALKALI OXIDIZERS	S3,S7	SOAP	F1,F7, F9	H9	E2,E9
LEVEL B ---		S5,S6	---	F6,F7	H11,H13	E1
LEVEL B VIN(+) VIT(0)	ALKALI METALS, Zn, AZIDES, HALOGENS, OXIDIZERS, AMINES	S1,S6, S7,S8	SOAP	F1,F7, F9	H4,H9	E1,E3,E4,E9
LEVEL B ---	HALOGENS, Fe, ALKALI METALS	S2,S5, S6	---	F4,F7	H9,H13	E1,E3,E9
LEVEL B VIN(-) VIT(-)	ALKALI METALS	S3,S7	SOAP	F6,F7, F9	H9	E1,E9
LEVEL B TEF(0) VIT(+) VIN(+)	ALKALI METALS,Zn, Mg,Al,PEROXIDES, HALOGENS,F,Ba, OXIDIZERS	S3,S7, S8	SOAP	F6,F7, F9	H2,H9	E1,E9
LEVEL A ---	WATER	S5,S6, S8	---	F1,F7 F8,F9	H6,H7, H8,H9	E2,E7
LEVEL A ---	OXIDIZERS	S2,S5, S6	---	F4,F7, F9	H6,H7, H8,H9	E2,E3,E9
LEVEL B ---	HALOGENS,WATER, P,Si,Zn,Sb,Bi, HEAT,OXIDIZERS	S9	---	F5,F8, F13	H9	E1,E7,E11, E16

CHEMICAL NAME	DOT #	CAS #	FORM	NFPA	VAPOR PRESS.	WATER SOL.
CESIUM	1407	7440-46-2	SIL. METAL	---	NONE	DEC.
CESIUM HYDROXIDE	2681 2682	21351-79-1	WHITE POWD.	---	NONE	S.
CESIUM NITRATE	1451	7789-18-6	WHITE POWD.	---	NONE	S.
CHLORDANE ***	2762	57-74-9	C. LIQ. > 1	---	---	0%
CHLORIC ACID	2626	7790-93-4	C. LIQ. > 1	---	---	S.
CHLORHYDRIN	2689	96-24-2	C. LIQ. > 1	---	LOW	S.
CHLORINATED CAMPHENE ***	2761	8001-35-2	YELL. SOL.	---	LOW	0%
CHLORINE ***	1017	7782-50-5	YELL. GAS	3-0-0 OX	GAS	S.
CHLORINE DIOXIDE ***	9191	10049-04-4	RED SOL.	---	HIGH	< 1%
CHLORINE TRIFLUORIDE	1749	7790-91-2	C. GAS	4-0-3 ~~W OX~~	GAS	DEC
CHLORINE PENTAFLUORIDE ***	2548	13637-63-3	GAS	---	GAS	DEC.
*** CHLORO-ACETALDEHYDE	2232	107-20-0	C. LIQ. > 1	---	HIGH	S.
CHLOROACETIC ACID ***	1750	79-11-8	WHITE POWD.	3-1-0	LOW	S.
CHLOROACETONE ***	1695	78-95-5	C. LIQ. > 1	---	---	S.

PPE	INCOMPATIBILITIES	SPILL	DECON.	FIRE	FIRST AID	SPECIAL
LEVEL A ---	WATER,ACIDS, HALOGENS, OXIDIZERS	S9	---	F5,F8, F12, F13	H6,H7, H8,H9	E1,E7,E16
LEVEL D BUT(-) NEO(-) VIN(-)	ACIDS	S3,S7	ACID	F6,F11	H8,H9	E1
LEVEL B ---	Al,COMBUSTIBLES	S3	WATER	F4,F7	H9	E1,E9,E13
LEVEL A TEF(0)	OXIDIZERS	S1,S7, S8	SOAP	F2,F7, F9	H1,H9	E1,E3,E9, E10
LEVEL A ---	NH₃,Sb,Bi,Fe,METAL SULFIDES, METAL CHLORIDES, COMBUSTIBLES	S3,S7	WATER	F4,F7, F10	H8,H9	E1,E7,E9, E14,E16
LEVEL A ---	OXIDIZERS	S3,S7	WATER	F1,F7, F9	H1,H9	E2,E9
LEVEL A ---	OXIDIZERS	S3,S7, S8	SOAP	F6,F7, F9	H2,H9	E2,E9
LEVEL A TEF(+) SAR(+) NEO(+)	COMBUSTIBLES, REDUCING AGENTS, POWDERED METALS	S4,S5	---	F4,F7, F8,F9 F10	H6,H7, H8,H9	E2,E7,E9, E16
LEVEL A ---	COMBUSTIBLES, HEAT,LIGHT	S3,S6, S7	FLOOD. WATER	F4,F7, F9, F10	H6,H7, H8,H9, H13	E2,E7,E9, E13
LEVEL A ---	COMBUSTIBLES,B, METALS AND SALTS, WATER,SILICATES, OXIDIZERS,ACIDS	S9	---	F5,F7, F8,F9, F10, F13	H6,H7, H8,H9	E2,E7,E9,E12 , E16
LEVEL A ---	METALS, WATER, COMBUSTIBLES, OXIDIZERS	S5,S6	---	F5,F8, F9,F11	H6,H7, H8,H9	E2,E7,E9, E16
LEVEL A ---	OXIDIZERS	S1,S7, S8	WATER	F1,F7, F9	H9	E2,E9
LEVEL B BUT(+) VIT(+) NEO(+)	OXIDIZERS	S3,S7	WATER	F2,F7, F9	H1,H6, H7,H8, H9	E2,E9
LEVEL A ---	OXIDIZERS, LIGHT	S1,S7	WATER	F1,F7, F9	H6,H7, H8,H9	E2,E3,E9

CHEMICAL NAME	DOT #	CAS #	FORM	NFPA	VAPOR PRESS.	WATER SOL.
CHLOROACETO-PHENONE ***	1697	532-27-4	WHITE POWD.	2-1-0	LOW	0%
CHLOROACETYL-CHLORIDE	1752	74-04-9	C. LIQ. > 1	3-0-1	MOD.	DEC
4-CHLOROANILINE ***	2018 2019	106-47-8	WHITE POWD.	---	LOW	< 1%
CHLOROFORM ***	1888	67-66-3	C. LIQ > 1	2-0-0	HIGH	0%
1-CHLORO-2-NITROBENZENE	1578	88-73-3	YELL. POWD.	3-1-0	LOW	0%
4-CHLOROPHENOL	2020 2021	106-48-9	WHITE POWD.	3-2-0	LOW	< 1%
CHLOROPICRIN ***	1580 1583 2929	76-06-2	C. LIQ. > 1	4-0-3	MOD.	0%
CHLOROPIVOYL-CHLORIDE ***	9263	4300-97-4	C. LIQ. > 1	---	---	DEC.
CHLOROPRENE	1991	126-99-8	C. LIQ. < 1	2-3-0	---	1%
2-CHLOROPROPANOL	2611	78-89-7	C. LIQ. > 1	2-2-0	---	S.
2-CHLOROPROPRENE	2456	557-98-2	C. LIQ. < 1	2-4-0	---	0%
2-CHLOROPYRIDINE	2822	109-09-1	C. LIQ. > 1	---	LOW	S.
CHLOROSULFONIC ACID ***	1754	7790-94-5	C. LIQ. > 1	---	LOW	DEC.
CHLORPYRIFOS® ***	2783	2921-88-2	WHITE POWD.	---	LOW	< 1%

PPE	INCOMPATIBILITIES	SPILL	DECON.	FIRE	FIRST AID	SPECIAL
LEVEL B ---	OXIDIZERS	S3,S7	SOAP	F1,F7, F9	H6,H7, H8,H9	E1,E9
LEVEL B ---	WATER,ALCOHOLS	S3,S6, S6	BASE	F6,F7, F9	H6,H7, H8,H9	E1,E7,E9, E12
LEVEL B BUT(-) VIN(-)	OXIDIZERS	S1,S7, S8	SOAP	F1,F7, F9	H1,H9, H12	E2,E9
LEVEL A VIN(+) VIT(-) TEF(0)	ALKALI METALS	S3,S6, S7,S8	SOAP	F6,F7, F9,F10	H2,H9	E1,E9
LEVEL B BUT(-) VIT(-)	OXIDIZERS	S1,S7	SOAP	F1,F7, F9	H1,H9, H12	E2,E3,E9
LEVEL B ---	OXIDIZERS	S1,S7	SOAP	F1,F7 F9	H1,H6, H7,H8, H9	E2,E9
LEVEL A TEF(0)	ALKALI, ANILINE ALKYNES, ALKALI	S3,S6, S7	SOAP	F6,F7, F9,F10	H1,H6, H7,H8, H9	E2,E9, E14
LEVEL A ---	WATER, ALKALI, ALCOHOLS, OXIDIZERS	S1,S7	BASE	F1,F7, F9	H6,H7, H8,H9	E1,E7,E9, E12
LEVEL A VIN(+) VIT(-)	OXIDIZERS	S1,S7	SOAP	F1,F7, F9	H9	E1,E3,E4,E5, E6,E9
LEVEL B BUT(-) VIT(-)	OXIDIZERS	S1,S7	WATER	F2,F7, F9	H9	E1,E9
LEVEL B ---	OXIDIZERS	S1,S7	SOAP	F2,F7, F9	H8,H9	E1,E3,E4, E5,E9
LEVEL A BUT(-)	OXIDIZERS	S1,S7	WATER	F1,F7, F9	H9	E2,E3,E9
LEVEL A TEF(0) SAR(0)	WATER,NITRATES, COMBUSTIBLES, ACIDS,POWD. METALS	S3,S7	FLOOD. WATER	F3,F8, F9,F11	H6,H7, H8,H9	E2,E7,E9, E16
LEVEL A ---	OXIDIZERS	S3,S7	SOAP	F1,F7, F9	H4,H9	E2,E9

CHEMICAL NAME	DOT #	CAS #	FORM	NFPA	VAPOR PRESS.	WATER SOL.
CHROMIC ACID ***	1463	1333-82-0	RED POWD.	3-0-1 OX	NONE	S.
CHROMIC NITRATE ***	2720	13548-38-4	BLUE POWD.	---	NONE	S.
CHROMYL- CHLORIDE ***	1758	14977-61-8	RED LIQ. > 1	3-0-2 W	---	DEC.
COAL TAR	1999	8007-45-2	BLACK LIQ.	---	---	0%
COPPER CYANIDE ***	1587	14765-77-0	YELL. POWD.	---	NONE	0%
COPPER NITRATE ***	1479	3251-23-8	BLUE POWD.	---	NONE	S.
m-CRESOL ***	2076	108-39-4	C. LIQ. > 1	3-2-0	LOW	0%
CROTONALDEHYDE ***	1143	4170-30-3	C. LIQ. < 1	3-3-2	MOD.	18%
CROTONIC ACID	2823	3724-65-0	WHITE POWD.	3-2-0	LOW	50%
CROTONLENE	1144	503-17-3	C. LIQ. < 1	---	HIGH	0%
CUMENE ***	1918	98-82-2	C. LIQ. < 1	2-3-1	MOD.	0%
CUMENE HYDROPEROXIDE	2116	80-15-9	C. LIQ. > 1	1-2-4 OX	LOW	< 1%
CYANOGEN ***	1026	460-19-5	C. GAS	4-4-2	GAS	S.
CYANOGEN BROMIDE ***	1889	506-68-3	WHITE POWD.	3-0-1	HIGH	S.

PPE	INCOMPATIBILITIES	SPILL	DECON.	FIRE	FIRST AID	SPECIAL
LEVEL A BUT(0) VIN(0)	COMBUSTIBLES,P, REDUCING AGENTS, HEAT,H₂S,HALOGENS	S3,S7	WATER	F4,F9, F10, F11	H6,H7, H8,H9	E2,E7,E13, E14
LEVEL D ---	COMBUSTIBLES, REDUCING AGENTS	S3,S7,	WATER	F4,F11 H12	H5,H9	E1,E9, E13
LEVEL A ---	LIGHT,WATER,P,S, REDUCING AGENTS, COMBUSTIBLES, AZIDES, HALIDES	S3,S7,	BASE	F6,F7, F9, F11	H6,H7, H8,H9	E1,E7,E9, E12
LEVEL A ---	OXIDIZERS	S1,S7,	SOAP	F1,F7, F9	H2,H9	E1,E9,E3
LEVEL A ---	OXIDIZERS,Mg	S3,S7, S8	ALK. HYPO- CHLOR.	F6,F7, F9	H9,H10	E2,E9
LEVEL B ---	Sn, COMBUSTIBLES, AMMONIA	S3,S7	WATER	F4,F9, F11, F12	H6,H7, H8,H9	E1,E9,E13
LEVEL B BUT(+) VIT(+)	OXIDIZERS	S1,S7, S8	SOAP	F1,F7, F9	H6,H7, H8,H9	E1
LEVEL B BUT(+) TEF(0)	OXIDIZERS, 1,3-BUTADIENE	S1,S6, S7,S8	WATER	F2,F7, F9	H6,H7, H8,H9	E2,E3,E6
LEVEL B ---	OXIDIZERS	S2,S3, S7	WATER	F1,F7	H6,H7, H8,H9	E1
LEVEL B ---	OXIDIZERS	S1,S6, S7, S8	SOAP	F1,F7,	H9	E1,E3,E4
LEVEL B VIT(0)	OXIDIZERS, ACIDS	S1,S6, S7, S8	SOAP	F2,F7, F9	H9	E1,E3,E5
LEVEL B TEF(0)	HEAT, ACIDS, REDUCING AGENTS, POWDERED METALS	S3,S7	WATER	F1,F7, F9,F10	H1,H8, H9	E1,E9,E13, E14,E16
LEVEL A ---	OXIDIZERS,ACIDS, WATER	S5,S6, S8	ALK. HYPO- CHLOR.	F1,F7, F9,F10	H8,H9, H10	E2,E3,E5,E7, E9
LEVEL A ---	HEAT, OXIDIZERS	S3, S6,S7, S8	ALK. HYPO- CHLOR.	F1,F7, F9	H6,H9, H10	E2,E3,E6, E7,E9

CHEMICAL NAME	DOT #	CAS #	FORM	NFPA	VAPOR PRESS.	WATER SOL.
CYANOGEN CHLORIDE ***	1589	506-77-4	C. LIQ. OR GAS	---	GAS	S.
CYANURIC CHLORIDE	2670	108-77-0	WHITE POWD.	---	LOW	DEC.
CYCLOHEXANE ***	1145	110-82-7	C. LIQ. < 1	1-3-0	HIGH	0%
CYCLOHEXANONE ***	1915	108-94-1	C. LIQ. < 1	---	MOD.	0%
CYCLOHEXYLAMINE	2357	108-91-8	C. LIQ. < 1	2-3-0	MOD.	S.
CYCLONITE	0072 0118	121-82-4	WHITE POWD.	---	NONE	0%
CYCLOOCTATRIENE	2538	629-20-9	YELL. LIQ. < 1	---	MOD.	0%
CYCLOPENTENE	2246	142-29-0	C. LIQ. < 1	1-3-1	---	0%
CYCLOPENTANONE	2245	120-92-3	C. LIQ. < 1	2-3-0	---	< 1%
CYCLOPROPANE	1027	75-19-4	C. GAS	1-4-0	GAS	0%
2,4-D ***	2765	94-75-7	WHITE POWD.	---	LOW	0%
DDT ***	2761	50-29-3	WHITE POWD.	---	NONE	0%
DECABORANE	1868	17702-41-9	WHITE POWD.	3-2-1	NONE	0%
DECAHYDRO-NAPHTHALENE	1147	91-17-8	C. LIQ. < 1	2-2-0	LOW	0%

PPE	INCOMPATIBILITIES	SPILL	DECON.	FIRE	FIRST AID	SPECIAL
LEVEL A ---	HEAT, OXIDIZERS	S2,S5, S6,S7, S8	ALK. HYPO-CHLOR.	F1,F7, F9	H6,H9	E2,E3,E6, E7,E9
LEVEL B ---	WATER, ACIDS, OXIDIZERS, ALCOHOLS	S3,S7	DRY	F1,F7, F8,F10	H6,H7, H8,H9, H10	E2,E7,E9,E16
LEVEL B NIT(+) VIT(+) TEF(0)	OXIDIZERS	S1,S6, S7,S8	SOAP	F2,F7,	H6,H9	E1,E3
LEVEL B BUT(+) TEF(+)	OXIDIZERS	S1,S6, S7,S8	SOAP	F2,F7	H6,H9	E1,E3
LEVEL B ---	OXIDIZERS, HALOGENS	S1,S6, S7	WATER	F2,F7, F9	H1,H6, H7, H8,H9	E1,E3,E9
LEVEL A ---	OXIDIZERS, COMBUSTIBLES	S9	---	F1,F7, F9,F10	H6,H7, H8,H9	E1,E8,E9, E16
LEVEL B ---	OXIDIZERS	S1,S7	SOAP	F1,F7	H9	E1,E3,E5
LEVEL B ---	OXIDIZERS	S1,S6, S7	SOAP	F1,F7	H9	E1,E3
LEVEL B ---	OXIDIZERS	S1,S6, S7	SOAP	F2,F7	H9	E1,E3
LEVEL B ---	OXIDIZERS	S2,S5, S6	---	F1,F7	H9	E1,E3
LEVEL B RUB(+) NEO(+) VIN(+)	OXIDIZERS	S1,S7, S8	SOAP	F1,F7, F9	H1,H9	E2,E9
LEVEL B ---	OXIDIZERS	S1,S7, S8	SOAP	F1,F7, F9	H2,H9	E1,E9,E10
LEVEL B ---	OXIDIZERS,ETHERS, HALOCARBONS	S1,S7	SOAP	F4,F5, F7,F9	H8,H9	E2,E7,E8, E16
LEVEL B ---	OXIDIZERS	S1,S7	SOAP	F1,F7, F9	H1,H9	E1,E3,E9

CHEMICAL NAME	DOT #	CAS #	FORM	NFPA	VAPOR PRESS.	WATER SOL.
DIACETONE ALCOHOL	1148	123-42-2	C. LIQ. < 1	1-2-0	LOW	S.
DIACETAL	2346	431-03-8	YELL. LIQ. < 1	1-3-0	---	25%
DIALLYLAMINE	2359	124-02-7	C. LIQ. < 1	---	MOD.	S.
DIALLYL ETHER	2360	557-40-4	C. LIQ. < 1	3-3-2	---	0%
DIAZINON ***	2783	333-41-5	C. LIQ. > 1	---	LOW	0%
DIBORANE ***	1911	19287-45-7	C. GAS	3-4-3 W	GAS	DEC.
1,2-DIBROMO-3-CHLOROPROPANE ***	2872	96-12-8	YELL. LIQ. > 1	---	---	0%
1,2-DIBROMOETHANE ***	1605	106-93-4	C. LIQ. > 1	---	MOD.	0%
DIBROMOMETHANE	2664	74-95-3	C. LIQ. > 1	---	MOD.	0%
n-DIBUTYLAMINE	2248	111-92-2	C. LIQ. < 1	3-2-0	LOW	0%
DICHLOROACETIC ACID	1764	79-43-6	C. LIQ. > 1	---	LOW	S.
DICHLOROACETYL CHLORIDE	1765	79-36-7	FUM. LIQ. > 1	3-2-1 W	---	DEC.
3,4-DICHLORO-ANILINE	1590	95-76-1	BRN. POWD.	3-1-0	LOW	0%
o-DICHLORO-BENZENE ***	1591	95-50-1	C. LIQ. > 1	2-2-0	LOW	0%

PPE	INCOMPATIBILITIES	SPILL	DECON.	FIRE	FIRST AID	SPECIAL
LEVEL B NEO(0)	OXIDIZERS	S1,S7	WATER	F1,F7	H9	E1,E3,E4
LEVEL B ---	OXIDIZERS	S1,S7	WATER	F2,F7	H9	E1,E3
LEVEL B VIN(0) VIT(0)	OXIDIZERS, ACID CHLORIDES, ANHYDRIDES	S1,S6, S7	WATER	F2,F7, F9	H6,H7, H8,H9	E1,E3,E9
LEVEL B ---	OXIDIZERS	S1,S7	SOAP	F2,F7, F9	H9	E2,E3,E4,E5
LEVEL A ---	OXIDIZERS	S1,S7	SOAP	F1,F7, F9	H3,H9	E2
LEVEL A ---	WATER,HALOGENS, OXIDIZERS, Al, Li, HALOCARBONS, ACIDS	S2,S4, S5	---	F4,F7, F9,F10	H8,H9	E2,E7,E9, E16
LEVEL B ---	OXIDIZERS	S1,S7, S8	SOAP	F1,F7, F9	H2,H9	E1,E9
LEVEL B ---	OXIDIZERS	S3,S6, S7	SOAP	F1,F7, F9	H1,H3, H9	E1
LEVEL B VIN(0)	ALKALI METALS, OXIDIZERS	S1,S6, S7	SOAP	F1,F7, F9	H9	E1,E9
LEVEL B BUT(+) VIN(+) VIT(+)	ACID CHLORIDES,CO2, ACID ANHYDRIDES, OXIDIZERS	S1,S7	SOAP	F4,F7	H6,H7, H8,H9	E2,E3,E9
LEVEL B ---	OXIDIZERS	S1,S7	BASE	F1,F7, F9	H1,H6, H7,H8, H9	E1,E9
LEVEL B VIT(-)	WATER, ALCOHOLS, OZIDIZERS	S1	FLOOD WATER	F3,F4, F7,F8	H1,H6, H7,H8, H9	E2,E7,E9, E12
LEVEL A ---	ACIDS, OXIDIZERS	S1,S7	SOAP	F1,F7, F9	H5,H6, H7,H8, II9,II12	E2,E9,E12
LEVEL B VIT(0)	OXIDIZERS, Al and ALLOYS	S1,S7, S8	SOAP	F1,F7, F9	H1,H5, H9	E1,E9

CHEMICAL NAME	DOT #	CAS #	FORM	NFPA	VAPOR PRESS.	WATER SOL.
DICHLORODIETHYL ETHER ***	1916	111-44-4	C. LIQ. > 1	3-2-1	LOW	0%
DICHLORO-DIFLUOROMETHANE ***	1028	75-71-8	GAS	---	GAS	0%
1,1-DICHLORO-ETHANE ***	2362	75-34-5	C. LIQ. > 1	2-3-0	HIGH	0%
1,2-DICHLORO-ETHYLENE ***	1150	540-59-0	C. LIQ. > 1	2-3-2	HIGH	0%
DICHLORO-DIISOPROPYL ETHER ***	2490	108-60-1	C. LIQ. > 1	2-2-0	LOW	0%
1,1-DICHLORO-1-NITROETHANE	2650	594-72-9	C. LIQ. > 1	2-2-3	MOD.	0%
DICHLOROPENTANE	1152	628-76-2	C. LIQ. > 1	2-3-2	---	0%
DICHLOROPHENYL TRICHLOROSILANE	1766	27137-85-5	C. LIQ. > 1	---	---	DEC.
1,3-DICHLORO-PROPENE ***	2047	542-75-6	C. LIQ. > 1	3-3-0	MOD.	0%
2,2-DICHLORO-PROPIONIC ACID ***	1760	75-99-0	C. LIQ. > 1	---	---	S.
DICHLOROSILANE ***	2189	4109-96-0	C. GAS	3-4-2 W	GAS	DEC.
3,5-DICHLORO-2,4,6-TRIFLUORO-PYRIDINE ***	9264	1737-93-5	C. LIQ. > 1	---	---	---
DICHLORVOS® ***	2783	62-73-7	C. LIQ. > 1	---	LOW	1%
DICYCLOHEXYL-AMINE	2565	101-83-7	C. LIQ. < 1	3-1-0	MOD.	< 1%

PPE	INCOMPATIBILITIES	SPILL	DECON.	FIRE	FIRST AID	SPECIAL
LEVEL B ---	ACIDS, OXIDIZERS	S1	SOAP	F1,F7, F9	H6,H7, H8,H9	E1,E5,E7, E9
LEVEL B ---	Al, Mg, Ag, Cu and ALLOYS	S5,S6, S8	---	F1,F7, F9	H9,H11	E1,E9
LEVEL B ---	OXIDIZERS	S1,S6, S7,S8	SOAP	F1,F7, F9	H1,H9	E1,E3,E9
LEVEL B ---	OXIDIZERS, ALKALI METALS, N$_2$O$_4$	S1,S6, S7,S8	SOAP	F1,F7, F9	H9	E1,E3,E8,E9
LEVEL B ---	OXIDIZERS	S1,S7, S8	SOAP	F1,F7, F9	H1,H6, H7,H8, H9	E2,E3,E5, E9
LEVEL B ---	OXIDIZERS	S1,S6, S7	SOAP	F1,F7, F9	H6,H7, H9	E2,E3,E9, E14
LEVEL B ---	OXIDIZERS	S1,S7	SOAP	F1,F7, F9	H9	E1,E3,E9
LEVEL A ---	OXIDIZERS, WATER	S1,S7	BASE	F1,F7, F8,F9	H6,H7, H8,H9	E2,E7,E9, E12
LEVEL A VIN(+) VII(+)	OXIDIZERS, ACIDS, METALS	S1,S6, S7,S8	SOAP	F1,F7, F9	H6,H7, H8,H9	E2,E3,E9
LEVEL B ---	OXIDIZERS	S1,S7	SOAP	F1,F7, F9	H6,H7, H8,H9	E2,E9
LEVEL A ---	WATER, AIR, OXIDIZERS	S2,S5, S6	---	F4,F7, F9,F10	H6,H7, H8,H9	E2,E3,E4,E7, E9,E11,E12
LEVEL B ---	OXIDIZERS	S1,S7	SOAP	F1,F7, F9	H9	E1,E9
LEVEL A ---	ACIDS, ALKALI, OXIDIZERS	S1,S7	SOAP	F1,F7, F9	H7,H9	E2,E9
LEVEL B ---	ACID CHLORIDES, ANHYDRIDES, CHLOROFORMATES, OXIDIZERS	S1,S6, S7	SOAP	F1,F7, F9	H1,H6, H7,H8, H9	E2,E9

CHEMICAL NAME	DOT #	CAS #	FORM	NFPA	VAPOR PRESS.	WATER SOL.
DICYCLOHEXYL-AMMONIUM NITRATE	2687	3129-91-7	WHITE POWD.	---	NONE	---
DICYCLO-PENTADIENE	2048	77-73-6	C. LIQ. > 1	1-3-1	MOD.	0%
DIELDRIN® ***	2761	60-57-1	WHITE POWD.	---	---	0%
DIETHOXY-DIMETHYLSILANE	2380	78-62-6	C. LIQ. < 1	---	MOD.	DEC.
DIETHYLAMINE ***	1154	109-89-7	C. LIQ. < 1	3-3-0	HIGH	S.
DIETHYLAMINO-ETHANOL	2686	100-37-8	C. LIQ. < 1	3-2-0	LOW	S.
DIETHYLALUMINUM CHLORIDE	1101	96-10-6	C. LIQ. < 1	3-4-3 W	LOW	DEC.
DIETHYLAMINO-PROPYLAMINE	2684	104-78-9	C. LIQ. < 1	---	---	S.
DIETHYLANILINE	2432	91-66-7	YELL. LIQ < 1	3-2-2	LOW	15%
DIETHYLBENZENE	2049	25430-17-4	C. LIQ. < 1	2-2-0	LOW	0%
2-DIETHYL-DICHLORO-SILANE	1767	1719-53-5	C. LIQ. > 1	---	---	DEC.
DIETHYL-CARBONATE	2366	105-58-8	C. LIQ. < 1	2-3-1	MOD.	0%
DIETHYLENE-TRIAMINE	2079	111-40-0	YELL. LIQ. < 1	3-1-0	LOW	S.
DIETHYL ETHER	1155	60-29-7	C. LIQ. < 1	2-4-1	HIGH	0%

PPE	INCOMPATIBILITIES	SPILL	DECON.	FIRE	FIRST AID	SPECIAL
LEVEL B ---	ACID CHLORIDES, ANHYDRIDES, CHLOROFORMATES, OXIDIZERS	S1,S7	SOAP	F1,F7, F9	H9,H12	E1,EP
LEVEL B ---	OXIDIZERS	S1,S6, S7	SOAP	F2,F7	H9	E1,E3
LEVEL A ---	Cu, Fe, OXIDIZERS	S3,S7, S8	SOAP	F1,F7, F9	H1,H9	E2,E9
LEVEL B ---	WATER, OXIDIZERS	S1,S6, S7	SOAP	F2,F7, F9	H9	E1,E3,E7,E9
LEVEL B TEF(-)	OXIDIZERS, ACIDS, HALOGENS	S1,S6, S7	WATER	F2,F7, F9	H5,H6, H7,H8, H9	E1,E3,E9
LEVEL B BUT(+) VIT(+) VIN(+) NIT(+)	OXIDIZERS	S1,S7	WATER	F1,F7, F9	H5,H6, H7,H8, H9	E1,E3
LEVEL A ---	WATER, AIR, ACIDS, ALCOHOLS, AZIDES, OXIDIZERS	S9	---	F5,F7, F8,F9	H6,H7, H8,H9	E2,E7,E9, E10,E11, E12,E16
LEVEL A ---	ACID CHLORIDES, ANHYDRIDES, CHLOROFORMATES, OXIDIZERS	S1,S7	WATER	F1,F7, F9	H6,H7, H8,H9	E2
LEVEL A ---	OXIDIZERS	S1,S7	WATER	F1,F7	H9,H12	E1,E3
LEVEL D ---	OXIDIZERS	31,37	3OAP	F1,F7, F9	H9	E1,E3,E9
LEVEL B VIT(+) NIT(+)	WATER, OXIDIZERS	S1,S3	BASE	F1,F7, F8,F9	H6,H7, H8,H9	E1,E3,E7, E9,E12
LEVEL B ---	OXIDIZERS	S1,S6, S7	SOAP	F1,F7	H1,H9	E1,E3
LEVEL B BUT(+)	OXIDIZERS, ACIDS, HALOGENS, Cu and ALLOYS	S1,S7	WATER	F2,F7, F9	H6,H7, H8,H9	E2,E3
LEVEL B TEF(+) VIN(+)	OXIDIZERS	S1,S6, S7	SOAP	F2,F7	H9	E1,E3,E4, E5

CHEMICAL NAME	DOT #	CAS #	FORM	NFPA	VAPOR PRESS.	WATER SOL.
DIETHYL KETONE	1156	96-22-0	C. LIQ. < 1	1-3-0	MOD.	2%
DIETHYL SULFATE	1594	64-67-5	C. LIQ. > 1	3-1-1	LOW	0%
DIETHYL ZINC	1366	557-20-0	C. LIQ. > 1	1-4-3 W	---	DEC.
DIHYDROPYRAN	2376	110-87-2	C. LIQ. < 1	2-3-0	---	0%
DIISOBUTYL-KETONE	1157	108-83-8	C. LIQ. < 1	1-2-0	LOW	0%
DIISOPROPYL-AMINE	1158	108-18-9	C. LIQ. < 1	3-3-0	HIGH	< 1%
DIISOPROPYL PEROXY-DICARBONATE	2133 2134	105-64-6	WHITE POWD.	---	NONE	0%
DIKETENE ***	2521	674-82-8	C. LIQ. > 1	3-2-2	MOD.	DEC.
1,2-DIMETHOXY-ETHANE	2252	110-71-4	C. LIQ. < 1	2-2-0	HIGH	0%
DIMETHYLAMINE ***	1032 1160	124-40-3	C. GAS	3-4-0	GAS	S.
DIMETHYL-AMINOETHANOL	2051	108-01-0	C. LIQ. < 1	2-2-0	LOW	S.
N,N-DIMETHYL-ANILINE	2253	121-69-7	YELL. LIQ. < 1	3-2-0	LOW	2%
1,3-DIMETHYL BUTYLAMINE	2379	108-09-8	C. LIQ. < 1	2-3-0	---	0%
*** DIMETHYLCARB-AMOYL CHLORIDE	2262	79-44-7	C. LIQ. > 1	---	---	DEC.

PPE	INCOMPATIBILITIES	SPILL	DECON.	FIRE	FIRST AID	SPECIAL
LEVEL B ---	OXIDIZERS	S1,S6, S7	SOAP	F2,F7	H9	E1,E3
LEVEL A ---	HEAT, BASE, Fe, OXIDIZERS	S1,S7	SOAP	F1,F7, F9	H6,H7, H8,H9	E2,E7,E9,E14
LEVEL B ---	HALOGENS,WATER, AIR,COMBUSTIBLES, SO₂, PCl₃	S9	---	F3,F8, F9,F1 0F11	H6,H7, H8,H9	E2,E3,E7, E10,E11, E14,E16
LEVEL B ---	OXIDIZERS	S1,S6, S7	SOAP	F2,F7	H9	E1,E3,E4,E5
LEVEL B VIN(0)	OXIDIZERS	S1,S7	SOAP	F2,F7	H9	E1,E3
LEVEL B TEF(+) VIT(+)	OXIDIZERS	S1,S6, S7	SOAP	F1,F7, F9	H6,H7, H8,H9	E1,F3,E9
LEVEL B ---	KI, COMBUSTIBLES, AMINES	S1,S7	SOAP	F1,F7, F11	H9	E1,E8,E13, E14
LEVEL B ---	ACIDS, OXIDIZERS, HALOCARBONS, BASES, METALS	S1,S7	SOAP	F1,F7, F9,F1 0	H6,H7, H8,H9	E2,E3,E6, E14
LEVEL B BUT(0)	OXIDIZERS	S1,S6, S7	SOAP	F1,F7	H9	E1,E3,E5
LEVEL B BUT(+) NEO(+)	ACIDS,HALOGENS, Zn,Sn,Al,Hg,ACID CHLORIDES,OXIDIZERS	S2,S5, S6,S7	WATER	F2,F7	H6,H7, H8,H9	E1,E3,E10
LEVEL B BUT(+) NIT(+)	ACIDS,Cu,Cu ALLOYS, Zn,OXIDIZERS	S1,S7	WATER	F2,F7	H6,H7, H8,H9	E1,E3
LEVEL B ---	ACID CHLORIDES, ANHYDRIDES, CHLOROFORMATES, OXIDIZERS	S1,S7	SOAP	F1,F7, F9	H9,H12	E2,E3,E9
LEVEL B VIT(+) NIT(+) VIN(+)	OXIDIZERS, HALOGENS	S1,S7	SOAP	F1,F7	H6,H7, H8,H9	E1,E3,E9
LEVEL B ---	OXIDIZERS, WATER	S1,S7, S8	FLOOD. WATER	F1,F7, F9	H6,H7, H8,H9	E1,E3,E7,E9

CHEMICAL NAME	DOT #	CAS #	FORM	NFPA	VAPOR PRESS.	WATER SOL.
DIMETHYL CHLOROTHIO-PHOSPHATE ***	2267	2524-03-0	WHITE POWD.	---	LOW	DEC.
DIMETHYL-DISULFIDE	2381	624-92-0	C. LIQ. > 1	---	MOD.	---
DIMETHYL ETHER	1033	115-10-6	C. GAS	2-4-1	GAS	S.
DIMETHYL-FORMAMIDE	2265	68-12-2	C. LIQ. < 1	1-2-0	LOW	S.
1,1-DIMETHYL-HYDRAZINE ***	1163	57-14-7	C. LIQ. < 1	3-3-1	HIGH	S.
DIMETHYL SULFATE ***	1595	77-78-1	C. LIQ. > 1	4-2-0	LOW	0%
DIMETHYL SULFIDE	1164	75-18-3	C. LIQ. < 1	2-4-0	HIGH	0%
DIAMINOPHENYL METHANE	2651	101-77-9	WHITE POWD.	---	NONE	< 1%
2,4-DINITROANILINE	1596	97-02-9	YELL. POWD.	3-1-3	---	0%
1,3-DINITROBENZENE **	1597	99-65-0	YELL. POWD.	3-1-4	---	0.2%
DINITRO-o-CRESOL ***	1598	534-52-1	YELL. POWD.	---	LOW	0%
2,4-DINITROPHENOL ***	1320 1321 1599	51-28-5	YELL. POWD.	---	---	< 1%
2,4-DINITROTOLUENE ***	1600 2038	121-14-2	YELL. POWD.	3-1-3	LOW	0%
DIOXANE ***	1165	123-91-1	C. LIQ. < 1	2-3-1	MOD.	S.

PPE	INCOMPATIBILITIES	SPILL	DECON.	FIRE	FIRST AID	SPECIAL
LEVEL A ---	OXIDIZERS	S1,S7	SOAP	F1,F7, F9	H6,H7, H8,H9	E1,E7,E9, E12,E14
LEVEL A ---	OXIDIZERS	S1,S6, S7	SOAP	F1,F7, F9	H9	E2,E3,E9
LEVEL B BUT(+) NEO(+)	OXIDIZERS, HYDRIDES, HALOGENS	S2,S5, S6	---	F2,F7, F9	H9	E1,E3,E4, E5
LEVEL B BUT(+) TEF(+)	OXIDIZERS,REDUCING AGENTS,HALOGENS, HALOCARBONS	S1,S7	WATER	F2,F7	H9	E1,E3,E9
LEVEL A BUT(+)	OXIDIZERS,Hg, HALOGENS, PEROXIDES	S1,S6, S7,S8	WATER	F2,F7, F9	H2,H6, H7,H8, H9	E2,E3,E4
LEVEL A ---	OXIDIZERS, NH₃, BASES	S1,S7, S8	WATER	F1,F7, F9	H6,H7, H8,H9	E2,E9
LEVEL B ---	OXIDIZERS	S1,S6, S7	SOAP	F1,F7, F9	H9	E1,E3,E9
LEVEL B ---	OXIDIZERS	S1,S7	SOAP	F1,F7, F9	H2,H9	E1,E9
LEVEL B ---	OXIDIZERS, HALOGENS, ACID CHLORIDES	S1,S7	SOAP	F1,F7, F9,F10	H9,H12	E2,E8,E14
LEVEL B ---	OXIDIZERS	S1,S7	SOAP	F1,F7, F9,F10	H9,H12	E2,E8,E14
LEVEL B ---	OXIDIZERS	S1,S7, S8	SOAP	F1,F7, F9,F10	H9,H12	E2,E8,E14
LEVEL B ---	ALKALI, AMMONIA, OXIDIZERS	S1,S7, S8	SOAP	F1,F7, F9,F10	H9	E2,E8,E10, E14,E16
LEVEL A SAR(+)	OXIDIZERS	S1,S7, S8	SOAP	F1,F7, F9,F10	H9,H12	E2,E8,E14, E17
LEVEL B BUT(0) VIN(0) TEF(0)	OXIDIZERS, HALOGENS, SO₃	S1,S6, S7,S8	SOAP	F2,F7, F9	H2,H9	E1,E3,E4, E5

CHEMICAL NAME	DOT #	CAS #	FORM	NFPA	VAPOR PRESS.	WATER SOL.
DIVINYL ETHER	1167	109-93-3	C. LIQ. < 1	2-3-2	---	0%
ENDRIN ***	2761	72-20-8	WHITE POWD .	---	LOW	0%
EPICHLOROHYDRIN ***	2023	106-89-8	C. LIQ. > 1	3-3-2	MOD.	7%
ETHANOLAMINE	2491	141-43-5	C. LIQ. 1.0	2-2-0	LOW	S.
ETHION ***	2783	563-12-2	C. LIQ. > 1	---	LOW	< 1%
ETHYL ACETATE ***	1173	141-78-6	C. LIQ. < 1	1-3-0	HIGH	< 1%
ETHYL ACRYLATE ***	1917	140-88-5	C. LIQ. < 1	2-3-2	MOD.	0%
ETHYLAMINE	1036 2270	75-04-7	C. LIQ. < 1	3-4-0	HIGH	S.
N-ETHYLANILINE	2272	103-69-5	YELL. LIQ. < 1	3-2-0	LOW	0%
2-ETHYLANILINE	2273	578-54-1	YELL. LIQ. 1.0	---	LOW	S.
ETHYLBENZENE ***	1175	100-41-4	C. LIQ. < 1	2-3-0	MOD.	0%
ETHYL CHLOROACETATE	1181	105-39-5	C. LIQ. > 1	---	MOD.	0%
ETHYL CHLORIDE	1037	75-00-3	C. LIQ. < 1	2-4-0	HIGH	0%

PPE	INCOMPATIBILITIES	SPILL	DECON.	FIRE	FIRST AID	SPECIAL
LEVEL B ---	OXIDIZERS	S1,S6, S7	SOAP	F1,F7, F9	H9	E1,E3,E4, E5,E6
LEVEL A ---	OXIDIZERS	S1,S7, S8	SOAP	F1,F7, F9	H1,H9	E2,E9,E10
LEVEL B BUT(+) TEF(0)	ACIDS, ALKALI,K,Zn, ALKALI,FeCl₃,AlCl₃,Al, AMINES,	S1,S6, S7,S8	SOAP	F2,F7, F9,F10	H2,H8, H9	E2,E3,E6
LEVEL B BUT(+) NEO(+) NIT(+) VIT(+)	ACIDS, ANHYDRIDES, ACROLEIN,CELLULOSE ACRYLONITRILE, EPICHLOROHYDRIN, VINYL CHLORIDE	S1,S7	WATER	F2,F7, F9	H6,H7, H8,H9	E1,E9
LEVEL A TEF(0)	OXIDIZERS	S1,S7	SOAP	F1,F7, F9	H9,H14	E2,E9
LEVEL B BUT(0) VIN(0) TEF(0)	OXIDIZERS,LITHIUM ALUMINUM HYDRIDE, CHLOROSULFONIC ACID,OXIDIZERS	S1,S6 S7,S8	SOAP	F2,F7	H9	E1,E3
LEVEL B BUT(+) VIN(+) TEF(+)	ACIDS,BASES, OXIDIZERS	S1,S6, S7,S8	SOAP	F2,F7	H6,H7, H8,H9	E2,E3,E6
LEVEL B BUT(+) TEF(0)	OXIDIZERS,Hg,Ag, BRASS,CELLULOSE NITRATE	S1,S6, S7	WATER	F1,F7, F9	H6,H7, H8,H9	E2,E3,E9
LEVEL B ---	OXIDIZERS	S1,S7	SOAP	F1,F7, F8	H9	E1
LEVEL B ---	OXIDIZERS	S1,S7	WATER	F1,F7, F9	H9,H12	E1,E9
LEVEL B VIT(+) TEF(0)	OXIDIZERS	S1,S6, S7	SOAP	F2,F7, F9	H9	E1,E3,E9
LEVEL B ---	OXIDIZERS, CYANIDES	S1,S6, S7	SOAP	F1,F7, F9	H9	E2,E3,E9
LEVEL B ---	Al,Cu,Mg,Zn,ALKALI METALS,OXIDIZERS	S2,S5, S6	SOAP	F1,F7, F8,F9	H9,H13	E1,E3,E9

CHEMICAL NAME	DOT #	CAS #	FORM	NFPA	VAPOR PRESS.	WATER SOL.
*** ETHYL CHLOROFORMATE	1182	541-41-3	C. LIQ. > 1	3-3-1	HIGH	DEC.
ETHYLENE	1038 1962	75-85-1	C. GAS	1-4-2	GAS	0%
ETHYLENE CHLOROHYDRIN ***	1135	107-07-3	C. LIQ. > 1	4-2-0	MOD.	S.
ETHYLENE DIAMINE ***	1604	107-15-3	C. LIQ. < 1	3-3-0	MOD.	S.
ETHYLENE DICHLORIDE ***	1184	107-06-2	C. LIQ. > 1	2-3-0	HIGH	0%
ETHYLENE GLYCOL DIETHYL ETHER	1153	629-14-1	C. LIQ. < 1	1-3-0	MOD.	0%
ETHYLENEIMINE ***	1185	151-56-4	C. LIQ. < 1	3-3-3	HIGH	S.
ETHYLENE OXIDE ***	1040	75-21-8	C. GAS	2-4-3	GAS	S.
ETHYL FORMATE	1190	109-94-4	C. LIQ. < 1	2-3-0	HIGH	0%
2-ETHYL-HEXYLAMINE	2276	104-75-6	C. LIQ. < 1	2-2-0	LOW	S.
ETHYL ISOCYANATE ***	2841	109-90-0	C. LIQ. < 1	---	MOD.	0%
ETHYL MERCAPTAN	2363	75-08-1	C. LIQ. < 1	2-4-0	HIGH	1%
ETHYL NITRITE	1194	109-95-5	C. LIQ. < 1	2-4-4	HIGH	DEC.
ETHYL PROPIONATE	1195	105-37-3	C. LIQ. < 1	---	MOD.	0%

PPE	INCOMPATIBILITIES	SPILL	DECON.	FIRE	FIRST AID	SPECIAL
LEVEL B ---	OXIDIZERS, RUST	S1,S6, S7	FLOOD. WATER	F2,F7, F8	H6,H7, H8,H9	E1,E3,E7, E9,E12
LEVEL B ---	OXIZIDERS, OXIDES, Cu and COMPOUNDS, HALOGENATED HYDROCARBONS, AlCl₃	S2,S5, S6	---	F1,F7	H9	E1,E3,E6, E8,E16
LEVEL A BUT(+) VIN(+) VIT(+)	ACIDS,BASES, ETHYLENE DIAMINE, STEAM,OXIDIZERS	S1,S6, S7	WATER	F1,F7, F9	H11	E2,E3,E4,E9
LEVEL B BUT(+) SAR(+)	ACIDS,ANHYDRIDES, ACROLEIN,CS₂, CHLOROCARBONS	S1,S6, S7,S9	WATER	F1,F7, F9	H6,H7, H8,H9	E2,E3,E9
LEVEL B TEF(+) VIT(+)	Al,NH₃,OXIDIZERS	S1,S6 S7,S8	SOAP	F1,F7, F9	H9	E1,E3,E4, E7,E9, E16
LEVEL B BUT(-)	OXIDIZERS	S1,S6, S7	SOAP	F2,F7	H9	E1,E3,E5
LEVEL A BUT(+)	ACIDS,CS₂,ACROLEIN, CHLORIDE SALTS, OXIDIZERS,Ag	S1,S6, S7,S8	WATER	F2,F7, F9	H6,H7, H8,H9	E2,E3,E4,E9
LEVEL A ---	ACIDS,BASES,Al,Fe, METAL OXIDES, AMINES	S2,S5, S6,S8	---	F2,F7, F9	H6,H9	E2,E3,E4, E6,E7
LEVEL B ---	OXIDIZERS	S1,S6, S7	SOAP	F2,F7, F9	H9	E1,E3,E9
LEVEL B ---	OXIDIZERS	S1,S7	WATER	F1,F7, F9	H6,H7, H8,H9	E1,E3,E9
LEVEL B ---	WATER,HEAT, OXIDIZERS	S1,S6, S7	SOAP	F2,F7, F9	H5,H6, H7,H8, H9	E1,E3,E9
LEVEL B ---	OXIDIZERS,STEAM	S1,S6, S7	SOAP	F1,F7, F9	H9	E1,E3,E4,E9
LEVEL B ---	HEAT,ACIDS, REDUCING AGENTS	S1,S6, S7	BASE	F1,F7, F9,F10	H6,H7, H8,H9, H12	E2,E3,E9,E14
LEVEL B TEF(-)	OXIDIZERS	S1,S6, S7	SOAP	F2,F7	H9	E1,E3

CHEMICAL NAME	DOT #	CAS #	FORM	NFPA	VAPOR PRESS.	WATER SOL.
ETHYL SILICATE	1292	78-10-4	C. LIQ. < 1	2-2-0	LOW	DEC.
ETHYL TRICHLOROSILANE	1196	115-21-9	C. LIQ. > 1	3-3-2 W̶	---	DEC.
FERRIC CHLORIDE ***	1773 2582	7705-08-0	BLACK SOL.	---	NONE	S.
FLUORINE ***	1045 9192	7782-41-4	YELL. GAS	4-0-4 W̶	GAS	DEC.
4-FLUOROANILINE	2941 2944	371-40-4	YELL. LIQ. > 1	---	---	S.
FLUOROBENZENE	2387	462-06-6	C. LIQ. 1.0	---	HIGH	0%
FLUORO-SULFONIC ACID	1777	7789-21-1	C. LIQ. > 1	---	---	DEC.
4-FLUORO-TOLUENE	2388	352-32-9	C. LIQ. 1.0	---	MOD.	0%
FORMALDEHYDE ***	1198 2209	50-00-0	C. GAS	3-4-0	GAS	S.
FORMIC ACID ***	1779	64-18-6	C. LIQ. > 1	3-2-0	MOD.	S.
FUMARYL CHLORIDE	1780	627-63-4	C. LIQ. > 1	---	---	DEC.
FURAN ***	2389	110-00-9	C. LIQ. < 1	1-4-1	HIGH	0%
FURFURAL ***	1199	98-01-1	C. LIQ. < 1	2-2-0	LOW	S.
FURFURYL ALCOHOL	2874	98-00-0	YELL. LIQ. > 1	1-2-1	LOW	S.

PPE	INCOMPATIBILITIES	SPILL	DECON.	FIRE	FIRST AID	SPECIAL
LEVEL B ---	OXIDIZERS	S1,S7	SOAP	F1,F7	H9	E1,E3
LEVEL B	WATER,OXIDIZERS	S1,S6, S7	FLOOD. WATER	F1,F7, F8	H6,H7, H8,H9	E1,E3,E7, E9,E12
LEVEL B ---	ALKALI METALS, ALLYL ALCOHOL, ETHYLENE OXIDE	S3	SOAP	F6,F7	H6,H7, H8,H9	E1
LEVEL A ---	COMBUSTIBLES, WATER	S5,S6, S8	---	F6,F7, F8,F9	H6,H7, H8,H9, H13	E2,E7,E9, E12,E16
LEVEL B ---	OXIDIZERS, ACID CHLORIDES	S1,S7	WATER	F1,F7, F8	H9,H12	E2,E9
LEVEL B ---	OXIDIZERS	S1,S6, S7	SOAP	F1,F7	H9	E1,E3
LEVEL A SAR(0)	ALCOHOLS, WATER	S1,S7	FLOOD. WATER	F3,F7, F8,F9 F14	H6,H7, H8,H9	E2,E7,E9
LEVEL B VIN(-) TEF(-) VIT(-)	OXIDIZERS	S1,S6, S7	SOAP	F1,F7	H9	E1,E3,E9
LEVEL B BUT(+) NIT(+) VIT(+) POLY(+)	OXIDIZERS	S2,S5, S6,S8	WATER	F1,F7, F9	H2,H5, H6,H7, H8,H9	E2,E3,E9
LEVEL B BUT(+) SAR(+)	OXIDIZERS,P_2O_5, POWDERED METALS, NITROMETHANE	S1,S6, S7,S8	WATER	F1,F7, F9	H6,H7, H8,H9	E1,E3
LEVEL B ---	ALCOHOLS, WATER	S3,S7	BASE	F1,F7, F8,F9	H6,H7, H8,H9	E2,E7,E9, E12
LEVEL B ---	OXIDIZERS	S1,S6, S7,S8	SOAP	F2,F7	H9	E1,E3,E4,E5
LEVEL B BUT(+)	OXIDIZERS,ACIDS, ALKALI	S1,S7, S8	WATER	F2,F7, F9	H5,H6, H7, H8,H9	E2,E6
LEVEL B ---	ACIDS, OXIDIZERS	S1,S7	WATER	F1,F7, F9	H9	E1,E3

CHEMICAL NAME	DOT #	CAS #	FORM	NFPA	VAPOR PRESS.	WATER SOL.
GASOLINE	1203 1257	8006-61-9	C. LIQ. < 1	1-3-0	---	0%
GERMANE ***	2192	7782-65-2	C. GAS	4-4-3	GAS	DEC.
GUANIDINE NITRATE	1467	506-93-4	WHITE POWD.	---	---	S.
HAFNIUM	1326 2545	7440-58-6	GREY POWD.	---	LOW	0%
HEXACHLORO- ACETONE	2661	116-16-5	C. LIQ. > 1	---	---	1%
HEXACHLORO- BENZENE ***	2729	118-74-1	WHITE POWD.	---	LOW	0%
HEXACHLORO- BUTADIENE ***	2279	87-68-3	C. LIQ. > 1	2-1-1	---	0%
HEXACHLORO- CYCLOPENTADIENE ***	2646	77-47-4	YELL. LIQ. > 1	---	LOW	0%
HEXACHLORO- ETHANE ***	9037	67-72-1	WHITE POWD. > 1	---	LOW	0%
HEXAFLUORO- ACETONE ***	2420	684-16-2	C. LIQ. ---	---	HIGH	---
HEXAFLUORO- PHOSPHORIC ACID	1782	16940-81-1	C. LIQ. > 1	---	---	S.
HEXALDEHYDE	1207	66-25-1	C. LIQ. < 1	2-3-1	MOD.	< 1%
HEXAMINE	1328	100-97-0	WHITE POWD. > 1	---	---	S.
HEXANE	1208	110-54-3	C. LIQ. < 1	1-3-0	HIGH	0%

PPE	INCOMPATIBILITIES	SPILL	DECON.	FIRE	FIRST AID	SPECIAL
LEVEL A NIT(+) TEF(+) VIT(+)	OXIDIZERS	S1,S4, S6,S7, S9	SOAP	F2,F7,	H1,H6, H9	E1,E3
LEVEL A	NUMEROUS CHEMICAL CLASSES	S2,S5, S6	---	F1,F7, F9	H6,H7, H8,H9	E2,E4,E7,E8, E11,E14,E16
LEVEL B ---	METALS, COMBUSTIBLES, OXIDIZERS	S3	WATER	F4,F7, F10	H9	E1,E8,E14
LEVEL B ---	OXIDIZERS,P,S,N$_2$, HALOGENS	S2,S3, S7	SOAP	F3,F5, F7,F8	H9	E1,E7,E8, E14,E16
LEVEL B ---	OXIDIZERS	S1,S7	SOAP	F6,F7, F9	H9	E1,E9
LEVEL B ---	DIMETHYL FORMAMIDE	S3,S8	SOAP	F1,F7, F9	H2,H9	E1,E9
LEVEL A ---	OXIDIZERS	S1,S7, S8	SOAP	F1,F7, F9	H1,H6, H7,H8, H9	E1,E6,E9
LEVEL A BUT(+) VIN(+) VIT(+)	OXIDIZERS,ALKALI METALS	S1,S7, S8	SOAP	F1,F7, F9	H6,H7, H8,H9	E2,E9
LEVEL B ---	OXIDIZERS	S3	SOAP	F6,F7, F9	H2,H9	E1,E9
LEVEL A ---	OXIDIZERS	S5,S6,S 7	SOAP	F6,F7, F9	H6,H7, H8,H9	E2,E3,E9
LEVEL B ---	ALKALI	S3,S7	FLOOD. WATER	F1,F7, F9	H6,H7, H8,H9	E2,E9
LEVEL B ---	OXIDIZERS	S1,S6, S7	SOAP	F2,F7	H9	E1,E3
LEVEL B ---	ACIDS	S1,S7	WATER	F1,F7, F9	H1,H9	E1,E7,E9
LEVEL B TEF(+) VIT(+) VIN(+) NIT(+)	OXIDIZERS	S1,S6, S7	SOAP	F1,F7	H9	E1,E3

CHEMICAL NAME	DOT #	CAS #	FORM	NFPA	VAPOR PRESS.	WATER SOL.
HEXANOIC ACID	1706	142-62-1	C. LIQ. < 1	2-1-0	LOW	0%
n-HEXANOL	2282	111-27-3	C. LIQ. < 1	1-2-0	LOW	1%
1-HEXENE	2370	592-41-6	C. LIQ. < 1	1-3-0	HIGH	0%
HYDRAZINE ***	2029 2030	302-01-2	C. LIQ./ POWD.	3-3-3	MOD.	S.
HYDROBROMIC ACID SOLUTION (>49%)	1788	10035-10-6	C. LIQ. ---	3-0-0	HIGH	S.
HYDROCHLORIC ACID SOLUTION (>30%)	1789	7647-01-0	C. LIQ. ---	---	HIGH	S.
HYDROCYANIC ACID	1051 1614	74-90-8	C. LIQ. < 1	4-4-2	HIGH	S.
HYDROFLUORIC ACID	1790	7664-39-3	C. LIQ. > 1	4-0-1	HIGH	S.
HYDROGEN	1049 1966	1333-74-0	C. GAS ---	0-4-0	GAS	0%
HYDROGEN BROMIDE ***	1048	10035-10-6	C. GAS ---	---	GAS	S.
HYDROGEN CHLORIDE ***	1050 2186	7647--01-1	C. GAS ---	3-0-0	GAS	S.
HYDROGEN CYANIDE ***	1613	74-90-8	C. GAS ---	4-4-2	GAS	S.
HYDROGEN FLUORIDE ***	1052	7664-39-3	C. GAS ---	4-0-1	GAS	S.
HYDROGEN PEROXIDE (35% - 52%)	2014	7722-84-1	C. LIQ. > 1	2-0-1 OX	LOW	S.

PPE	INCOMPATIBILITIES	SPILL	DECON.	FIRE	FIRST AID	SPECIAL
LEVEL B ---	OXIDIZERS	S3,S7	SOAP	F1,F7	H6,H7, H8,H9	E1
LEVEL B ---	OXIDIZERS	S1,S7	SOAP	F2,F7	H9,H15	E1
LEVEL B ---	OXIDIZERS	S1,S6, S7	SOAP	F1,F7	H9	E1,E3
LEVEL A BUT(+) NIT(+) VIN(+) TEF(+) SAR(+)	OXIDIZERS,Cu,Zn, COMBUSTIBLES,Fe, RUST, METAL SALTS, METAL OXIDES	S8,S9	---	F2,F7, F9,F10	H2,H4, H6,H7, H8,H9	E1,E3,E4,E7, E8,E9,E14, E16
LEVEL B BUT(+) NEO(+) SAR(+)	HALOGENS,FeO, NH₃,OZONE	S3,S6, S7	BASE	F6,F7, F9	H6,H7, H8,H9	E1,E9
LEVEL B BUT(+) SAR(+)	OXIDIZERS,CARBIDES, HALOGENS,REACTIVE Al,METALS	S3,S6, S7	BASE	F6,F7, F9	H6,H7, H8,H9	E1,E9
LEVEL A TEF(+)	ACETALDEHYDE, OXIDIZERS	S1,S6, S7,S8	ALK. HYPO-CHLOR.	F1,F7, F9	H9,H10	E2,E3,E4, E6,E7,E9
LEVEL A TEF(0)	REACTS WITH NUMEROUS CLASSES OF MATERIALS	S3,S6, S7,S8	BASE	F6,F7, F9	H8,H9	E2,E9
LEVEL B ---	OXIDIZERS,REACTIVE METALS,HALOGENS	S2,S5, S6	---	F1,F7	H9,H13	E1,E3,E4
LEVEL B BUT(+) NEO(+) SAR(+)	HALOGENS,FeO, NH₃,OZONE	S5,S6, S7	---	F6,F7, F9	H6,H7, H8,H9, H9,H13	E1,E9
LEVEL B BUT(+) SAR(+)	OXIDIZERS,CARBIDES, HALOGENS,REACTIVE Al,METALS	S5,S6, S7	---	F6,F7, F9	H6,H7, H8,H9, H9,H13	E1,E9
LEVEL A TEF(+)	ACETALDEHYDE, OXIDIZERS	S2,S5, S6,S8	---	F1,F7, F9	H9,H10	E2,E3,E4,E6
LEVEL A TEF(+)	REACTS WITH NUMEROUS CLASSES OF MATERIALS	S5,S6, S7,S8	---	F6,F7, F9	H6,H7, H8,H9	E2,E9
LEVEL B ---	COMBUSTIBLES, REDUCING AGENTS, POWDERED METALS	S3,S7	WATER	F2,F7	H6,H7, H8,H9	E1,E13,E16

CHEMICAL NAME	DOT #	CAS #	FORM	NFPA	VAPOR PRESS.	WATER SOL.
HYDROGEN SELENIDE ***	2202	7783-07-5	C. GAS ---	---	GAS	1%
HYDROGEN SULFIDE ***	1053	7783-06-4	C. GAS ---	3-4-0	GAS	S.
HYDROIODIC ACID	1787	10034-85-2	C. LIQ. > 1	3-0-0	---	S.
IMINOBIS-PROPYLAMINE	2269	56-18-8	C. LIQ. < 1	---	---	S.
IODINE MONOCHLORIDE	1792	7790-99-0	RED LIQ. > 1	---	---	S.
2-IODOBUTANE	2390	513-48-4	ORAN. LIQ. > 1	---	---	0%
IRON PENTACARBONYL ***	1994	13463-40-6	ORAN. LIQ. > 1	2-3-1 W	MOD.	DEC.
ISOBUTYL FORMATE	2393	542-55-2	C. LIQ. < 1	---	MOD.	1%
ISOBUTYLNITRILE	2284	78-82-0	C. LIQ. < 1	3-3-0	MOD.	1%
ISOPHORONE DIISOCYANATE ***	2290	4098-71-9	C. LIQ. > 1	---	LOW	---
ISOPRENE ***	1218	78-79-5	C. LIQ. < 1	2-4-2	HIGH	0%
ISOPROPANOL	1219	67-63-0	C. LIQ. < 1	1-3-0	MOD.	S.
ISOPROPYL ACETATE	1220	108-21-4	C. LIQ. < 1	1-3-0	MOD.	0%
ISOPROPENYL ACETATE	2403	108-22-5	C. LIQ. < 1	2-3-0	---	0%

PPE	INCOMPATIBILITIES	SPILL	DECON.	FIRE	FIRST AID	SPECIAL
LEVEL A ---	OXIDIZERS	S2,S5, S6,S7	---	F1,F7, F9	H5,H6, H9	E2,E3,E9
LEVEL B ---	OXIDIZERS,METAL OXIDES,HALOGENS, POWDERED METALS	S2,S5, S6	---	F1,F7, F9	H6,H7, H9	E2,E3,E4,E9
LEVEL B ---	OXIDIZERS, METALS, P	S3,S6, S7	WATER	F6,F7, F9	H6,H7, H8,H9	E1,E9
LEVEL B ---	OXIDIZERS,ACID CHLORIDES, HALOGENS	S1,S7	WATER	F1,F7, F9,F10	H6,H7, H8,H9	E2,E3,E14
LEVEL B ---	ALKALI METALS, P, REACTIVE METALS, COMBUSTIBLES, SULFIDES	S3,S7	WATER	F1,F7, F9,F10	H6,H7, H8,H9	E2,E7,E14
LEVEL B ---	OXIDIZERS	S1,S7	SOAP	F2,F7	H1,H9	E1,E3
LEVEL A ---	AIR,OXIDIZERS, COMBUSTIBLES, HALOGENS	S9	---	F1,F7, F9	H6,H7, H8,H9, H12	E2,E3,E11, E13,E14,E16
LEVEL B BUT(-) VIN(-)	OXIDIZERS	S1,S6, S7	SOAP	F1,F7, F9	H6,H7, H8,H9	E1,E3,E9
LEVEL B ---	OXIDIZERS	S1,S6, S7	ALK. HYPO-CHLOR.	F2,F7, F9	H9,H12	E2,E3,E9
LEVEL B BUT(+) VIN(+) VIT(+)	OXIDIZERS,AMINES, ALCOHOLS, ALKALI	S1,S7	SOAP	F1,F7, F9	H9	E1,E9
LEVEL B VIN(+) VIT(+)	OXIDIZERS,ACIDS, REDUCING AGENTS, LIGHT	S1,S7	SOAP	F1,F7, F9,F10	H9	E1,E3,E4, E6,E8,E14
LEVEL B NIT(+) NEO(0) TEF(0)	OXIDIZERS, Al	S1,S6, S7	WATER	F2,F7	H9	E1,E3
LEVEL B ---	OXIDIZERS	S1,S6, S7	SOAP	F2,F7	H9	E1,E3
LEVEL B ---	OXIDIZERS	S1,S7	SOAP	F2,F7	H9	E1,E3,E5

CHEMICAL NAME	DOT #	CAS #	FORM	NFPA	VAPOR PRESS.	WATER SOL.
ISOPROPENYL BENZENE	2303	98-83-9	C. LIQ. < 1	1-2-1	LOW	0%
ISOPROPYLAMINE	1221	75-31-0	C. LIQ. < 1	3-4-0	HIGH	S.
ISOPROPYL-CHLOROFORMATE ***	2407	108-23-6	C. LIQ. > 1	---	MOD.	0%
ISOPROPYL FORMATE	1281	625-55-8	C. LIQ. < 1	2-3-0	HIGH	DEC.
ISOPROPYL-MERCAPTAN	2402 2703	75-33-3	C. LIQ. < 1	---	HIGH	1%
ISOPROPYL NITRATE	1222	1712-64-7	C. LIQ. 1.0	---	---	0%
KEROSENE	1223	8008-20-6	C. LIQ. < 1	0-2-0	---	0%
LEAD ARSENATE ***	1617	7784-40-9	WHITE POWD.	2-0-0	NONE	0%
LEAD NITRATE ***	1469	10099-74-8	WHITE POWD.	---	NONE	50%
LEAD PERCHLORATE	1470	13637-76-8	WHITE POWD.	---	NONE	S.
LITHIUM	1415	7439-93-2	SILV METAL.	3-2-2 W	NONE	DEC.
LITHIUM ALUMINUM HYDRIDE	1410	16853-85-3	GREY POWD.	3-2-2 W	NONE	DEC.
LITHIUM AMIDE	1412	7782-89-0	WHITE POWD.	---	NONE	DEC.
LITHIUM BOROHYDRIDE	1413	16949-15-8	WHITE POWD.	---	NONE	DEC.

PPE	INCOMPATIBILITIES	SPILL	DECON.	FIRE	FIRST AID	SPECIAL
LEVEL B ---	OXIDIZERS	S1,S7	SOAP	F1,F7	H9	E1,E3
LEVEL B TEF(0)	OXIDIZERS	S1,S6, S7	WATER	F2,F7, F9	H6,H7, H8,H9	E1,E3,E4, E9
LEVEL B ---	ACIDS, WATER, IRON SALTS,ALKALI,AMINES	S1,S6, S7	SOAP	F1,F7, F9	H6,H7, H8,H9	E2,E3,E7, E9,E12
LEVEL B ---	OXIDIZERS, WATER	S1,S6, S7	BASE	F1,F7, F9	H9	E1,E3,E7,E9
LEVEL B ---	OXIDIZERS	S1,S6S 7	WATER	F1,F7, F7	H9	E1,E3,E9
LEVEL B ---	AIR,POWDERED METALS	S9	---	F1,F7, F9,F10	H9,H12	F1,F3,F8, E11,E14
LEVEL B NIT(+) VIN(+) VIT(0)	OXIDIZERS	S1,S7	SOAP	F1,F7, F9	H1,H9	E1,E3,E9
LEVEL B ---	---	S3,S7	SOAP	F6,F7, F9	H2,H9	E2,E9
LEVEL B ---	POWDERED METALS, THIOCYANATES, COMDUSTIBLES, HYPOPHOSPHITE	S3,S7	WATER	F4,F7, F9	H1,H9	E1,E9,E13
LEVEL B ---	ALCOHOLS,REDUCING AGENTS	S3,S7	WATER	F4,F7, F9	H9	E1,E16
LEVEL B ---	REACTS WITH NUMEROUS CLASSES OF COMPOUNDS	S9	---	F5,F7, F8	H8,H9	E2,E7,E12, E16
LEVEL B ---	REACTS WITH NUMEROUS CLASSES OF COMPOUNDS	S9	---	F5,F7, F8	H8,H9	E2,E7,E12, E16
LEVEL B ---	OXIDIZERS, WATER, ALCOHOLS,ACIDS	S3,S7	DRY	F5,F7, F9	H6,H7, H8,H9	E1,E7,E9, E12,E16
LEVEL B ---	ACIDS, WATER, ALCOHOLS	S3,S7	DRY	F5,F7, F9	H6,H7, H8,H9	E1,E7,E9, E12,E16

CHEMICAL NAME	DOT #	CAS #	FORM	NFPA	VAPOR PRESS.	WATER SOL.
LITHIUM HYDRIDE	1414 2805	7580-67-8	WHITE POWD.	---	NONE	DEC.
LITHIUM NITRIDE	2806	26134-62-3	RED POWD.	---	NONE	DEC.
MAGNESIUM	1418 1869 2950	7439-95-4	SILV. METAL	0-1-1	NONE	0%
MAGNESIUM CHLORATE	2723	10326-21-3	WHITE POWD.	---	NONE	S.
MAGNESIUM HYDRIDE	2010	60616-74-2	WHITE POWD.	---	NONE	DEC.
MAGNESIUM NITRATE	1474	13446-18-9	WHITE POWD.	---	NONE	S.
MALATHION ***	2783	121-75-5	BRN. LIQ. > 1	---	---	1%
MALEIC ANHYDRIDE ***	2215	108-31-6	WHITE POWD.	2-3-1	LOW	DEC.
MALONONITRILE ***	2647	109-77-3	WHITE POWD.	---	---	S.
MERCURIC ACETATE ***	1629	1600-27-7	WHITE POWD.	---	LOW	S.
MERCURIC CYANIDE ***	1636	592-04-1	WHITE POWD.	3-0-0	LOW	7%
MERCURIC NITRATE ***	1625	10045-94-0	WHITE POWD.	---	LOW	S.
MERCURY ***	2809	7439-97-6	SILV. METAL	---	LOW	0%
MESITYLENE	2325	1060-67-8	C. LIQ. < 1	0-2-0	LOW	0%

PPE	INCOMPATIBILITIES	SPILL	DECON.	FIRE	FIRST AID	SPECIAL
LEVEL B ---	ACIDS, ALCOHOLS, WATER, OXIDIZERS	S9	DRY	F5,F7, F8	H6,H7, H8,H9	E1,E7,E12, E16
LEVEL B ---	AIR, WATER	S9	DRY	F5,F7, F8,F9	H8,H9	E1,E7,E12, E16
LEVEL C ---	HALOGENS, METAL OXIDES, PHOSPHATES, HALOCARBONS, ACIDS	S3	SOAP	F5,F7	H9	E1,E7,E9, E16
LEVEL B ---	SULFIDES, Al, As, COMBUSTIBLES, ALCOHOLS	S3,S7	WATER	F4,F7, F9	H8,H9	E1,E13,E16
LEVEL B ---	AIR, WATER	S9	---	F5,F7, F8,F9	H8,H9	E1,E7,E11, E12,E16
LEVEL B ---	COMBUSTIBLES, REDUCING AGENTS	S3,S7	WATER	F4,F7	H9	E1,E13
LEVEL A NIT(+) TEF(+)	OXIDIZERS	S1,S7	SOAP	F1,F7, F9	H1,H5, H9,H14	E2,E9
LEVEL B ---	WATER, ALKALI METALS, OXIDIZERS, AMINES	S1,S7, S8	BASE	F1,F7	H1,H6, H7, H8,H9	E1,E6,E7, E12,E14, E16
LEVEL B ---	HEAT, ALKALI	S1,S7, S8	ALK. HYPO- CHLOR	F1,F7, F9	H9,H12	E2,E6,E9, E14,E16
LEVEL B ---	OXIDIZERS	S3,S7	WATER	F6,F7, F9	H9	E2,E9
LEVEL B ---	ACIDS, OXIDIZERS	S3,S7	ALK. HYPO- CHLOR.	F1,F7, F9	H9,H10	E2,E7,E9, E16
LEVEL B ---	COMBUSTIBLES, S, ACIDS	S3,S7	WATER	F4,F7, F9	H6,H7, H8,H9	E2,E13
LEVEL B ---	HALOGENS, NH3, OXIDIZERS, ACETYLENE	S3,S7, S8	SOAP	F2,F7, F9	H9	E2,E7,E16
LEVEL A ---	OXIDIZERS	S1,S7	SOAP	F2,F7	H9	E2,E3

CHEMICAL NAME	DOT #	CAS #	FORM	NFPA	VAPOR PRESS.	WATER SOL.
MESITYL OXIDE	1229	141-79-7	C. LIQ. < 1	3-3-1	MOD.	0%
METH-ACRYLALDEHYDE	2396	78-85-3	C. LIQ. < 1	3-3-2	HIGH	S.
METHACRYLIC ACID	2531	79-41-4	C. LIQ. 1.0	3-2-2	LOW	S.
METHACRYLO-NITRILE ***	3079	126-98-7	C. LIQ. < 1	2-3-2	HIGH	1%
METHALLYL ALCOHOL	2614	513-42-8	C. LIQ. < 1	2-3-0	---	S.
METHANESULFONYL CHLORIDE	9265	124-63-0	C. LIQ. > 1	---	---	DEC.
METHANOL ***	1230	67-56-1	C. LIQ. < 1	1-3-0	HIGH	S.
METHYL ACETATE	1231	79-20-9	C. LIQ. < 1	1-3-0	HIGH	S.
METHYL ACRYLATE	1919	96-33-3	C. LIQ. < 1	2-3-2	HIGH	0%
METHYLAL	1234	109-87-5	C. LIQ. < 1	2-3-2	HIGH	S.
METHYLALLYL CHLORIDE	2554	563-47-3	C. LIQ. < 1	---	HIGH	0%
METHYL ALUMINUM SESQUICHLORIDE	1927	12542-85-7	C. LIQ. > 1	---	---	DEC.
METHYLAMINE ***	1061	74-89-5	C. GAS	3-4-0	GAS	S.
N-METHYLANILINE	2294	100-61-8	C. LIQ. 1.0	---	LOW	< 1%

PPE	INCOMPATIBILITIES	SPILL	DECON.	FIRE	FIRST AID	SPECIAL
LEVEL B ---	OXIDIZERS,ACIDS, HALOGENS,BASES, REDUCING AGENTS	S1,S6, S7	SOAP	F2,F7, F9	H6,H7, H8,H9	E1,E3,E6
LEVEL B ---	OXIDIZERS,ACIDS, REDUCING AGENTS	S1,S6, S7	WATER	F2,F7, F9	H6,H7, H8,H9	E1,E3,E4, E6
LEVEL B BUT(+) VIT(+)	OXIDIZERS	S1,S7	WATER	F1,F7	H6,H7, H8,H9	E1,E3,E6
LEVEL A BUT(+)	OXIDIZERS	S1,S6, S7,S8	ALK. HYPO- CHLOR.	F2,F7, F9	H8,H9, H12	E2,E3,E6,E9
LEVEL B ---	OXIDIZERS	S1,S7	SOAP	F2,F7, F9	H9	E1,E3,E9
LEVEL A ---	ALCOHOLS, WATER, OXIDIZERS	S1,S6, S7	BASE	F1,F7, F9	H6,H7, H8,H9	E2,E7,E9, E12
LEVEL B BUT(+) VIT(+) TEF(+) SAR(+)	OXIDIZERS, HYDRIDES,REACTIVE METALS	S1,S6, S7,S8	WATER	F2,F7, F9	H9	E1,E3,E9
LEVEL B BUT(+)	OXIDIZERS	S1,S6, S7	SOAP	F2,F7, F9	H9	E1,E3,E4,E9
LEVEL B BUT(+) TEF(0)	OXIDIZERS,PEROXIDES	S1,S6, S7	SOAP	F2,F7, F9	H6,H7, H8,H9	E1,E3,E4,E5, E6,E9,E16
LEVEL B ---	OXIDIZERS	S1,S6, S7	WATER	F2,F7, F9	H9	E1,E3,E4,E5, E9
LEVEL B VIT(+)	OXIDIZERS	S1,S6, S7	SOAP	F2,F7, F9	H2,H9	E1,E3,E4,E5
LEVEL B ---	ALCOHOLS, WATER, OXIDIZERS, AIR	S9	---	F5,F7, F8,F9	H6,H7, H8,H9	E2,E3,E4,E7, E9,E11,E12, E16
LEVEL B BUT(+) NIT(+) VIT(+)	OXIDIZERS, NITRATED HYDROCARBONS, HALOGENS	S2,S5, S6	---	F1,F7, F9	H6,H7, H8,H9	E2,E3,E4,E9
LEVEL B ---	OXIDIZERS	S1,S7, S9	SOAP	F1,F7, F9	H9,H12	E1,E9

CHEMICAL NAME	DOT #	CAS #	FORM	NFPA	VAPOR PRESS.	WATER SOL.
METHYLBROMIDE ***	1062	74-83-9	C. GAS	3-1-0	GAS	0%
METHYL BUTANONE	2397	563-80-4	C. LIQ. < 1	---	MOD.	0%
3-METHYL-1-BUTENE	2561	563-45-1	C. LIQ. < 1	2-4-0	HIGH	0%
N-METHYL-BUTYLAMINE	2945	110-68-9	C. LIQ. < 1	3-3-0	---	S.
METHYL -tert-BUTYL ETHER	2398	1634-04-4	C. LIQ. < 1	---	HIGH	0%
METHYL n-BUTYRATE	1237	623-42-7	C. LIQ. < 1	2-3-0	MOD.	0%
METHYL CHLORIDE ***	1063	74-87-3	C. GAS	2-4-0	GAS	0%
METHYL CHLOROACETATE	2295	96-34-4	C. LIQ. > 1	2-2-1	MOD.	0%
*** METHYL CHLOROCARBONATE	1238	79-22-1	C. LIQ. > 1	---	HIGH	DEC.
METHYL CHLOROFORM ***	2831	71-55-6	C. LIQ. > 1	2-1-0	HIGH	0%
METHYL CHLOROMETHYL ETHER ***	1239	107-30-2	C. LIQ. > 1	---	HIGH	0%
METHYLCYCLO-HEXANE	2296	108-87-2	C. LIQ. < 1	2-3-0	MOD.	0%
METHYL-CYCLOPENTANE	2298	96-37-7	C. LIQ. < 1	2-3-0	HIGH	0%
METHYL DICHLOROACETATE	2299	116-54-1	C. LIQ. > 1	---	---	0%

PPE	INCOMPATIBILITIES	SPILL	DECON.	FIRE	FIRST AID	SPECIAL
LEVEL B VIN(0)	REACTIVE METALS, DIMETHYLSULFOXIDE, ETHYLENE OXIDE	S2,S5, S6,S8	---	F1,F7, F9,F10	H1,H6, H7, H8,H9	E2,E3,E9
LEVEL B ---	OXIDIZERS	S1,S6, S7	SOAP	F2,F7	H9	E1,E3
LEVEL B ---	OXIDIZERS	S1,S6, S7	SOAP	F2,F7	H9	E1,E3,E4
LEVEL B ---	OXIDIZERS	S1,S6, S7	SOAP	F1,F7, F9	H6,H7, H8,H9	E1,E3,E9
LEVEL B ---	OXIDIZERS	S1,S6, S7	SOAP	F2,F7	H6,H9	E1,E3,E4,E5
LEVEL B ---	OXIDIZERS	S1,S6, S7	SOAP	F2,F7	H9	E1,E3
LEVEL B ---	OXIDIZERS	S2,S5, S6,S8	---	F2,F7, F9,F10	H9	E1,E3,E4,E9
LEVEL B SAR(+)	OXIDIZERS	S1,S6, S7	SOAP	F1,F7, F9	H6,H7, H8,H9	E1,E3,E9
LEVEL B ---	WATER,ALCOHOLS, OXIDIZERS	S1,S6, S7,S8	BASE	F2,F7, F9	H6,H7, H8,H9	E2,E3,E7, E9,E12
LEVEL B VIN(+) VII(+) TEF(+)	OXIDIZERS, REACTIVE METALS & ALLOYS, ACETONE	S1,S6, S7,S8	SOAP	F1,F7, F9	H1,H9	E2,E3,E9
LEVEL A ---	OXIDIZERS, HEAT	S1,S6, S7	SOAP	F1,F7, F9	H2,H6, H7,H9	E1,E3,E5, E9
LEVEL B ---	OXIDIZERS	S1,S6, S7	SOAP	F1,F7	H9	E1,E3,E4
LEVEL B ---	OXIDIZERS	S1,S6, S7	SOAP	F2,F7	H9	E1,E3,E4
LEVEL B ---	ACIDS,OXIDIZERS	S1,S7	SOAP	F1,F7, F9	H6,H7, H8,H9	E1,E7,E9

CHEMICAL NAME	DOT #	CAS #	FORM	NFPA	VAPOR PRESS.	WATER SOL.
METHYL DICHLOROSILANE	1242	75-54-7	C. LIQ. > 1	3-3-2 W	HIGH	DEC.
METHYLENE BISPHENYL ISOCYANATE	2489	101-68-8	WHITE POWD.	---	LOW	0.2%
2-METHYL-5-ETHYLPYRIDINE	2300	104-90-5	C. LIQ. < 1	3-3-2	---	< 1%
METHYL HYDRAZINE ***	1244	60-34-4	C. LIQ. < 1	3-3-2	MOD.	S.
METHYL IODIDE ***	2644	78-88-4	C. LIQ. > 1	---	HIGH	S.
METHYL ISOBUTYL CARBINOL	2053	108-11-2	C. LIQ. < 1	2-2-0	LOW	2%
METHYL ISOCYANATE ***	2480	624-83-9	C. LIQ. < 1	4-3-2	HIGH	DEC.
METHYL ISOTHIOCYANATE	2477	556-61-6	WHITE SOL.	---	MOD.	<1%
METHYL MERCAPTAN ***	1064	74-93-1	C. GAS	2-4-0	GAS	S.
METHYL METHACRYLATE ***	1247	80-62-6	C. LIQ. < 1	2-3-2	MOD.	0%
METHYL MORPHOLINE	2535	109-02-4	C. LIQ. < 1	2-3-0	---	S.
METHYL PARATHION ***	2783	298-00-0	WHITE POWD.	---	---	0%
METHYLPENTANE	2462	96-14-0	C. LIQ. < 1	1-3-0	HIGH	0%
METHYL-PHOSPHONIC DICHLORIDE ***	9206	676-97-1	WHITE POWD.	---	---	DEC.

PPE	INCOMPATIBILITIES	SPILL	DECON.	FIRE	FIRST AID	SPECIAL
LEVEL B ---	OXIDIZERS,WATER, METAL OXIDES	S1,S6, S7	FLOOD. WATER	F1,F7, F8,F9	H6,H7, H8,H9	E2,E3,E4, E7,E9,E12
LEVEL A ---	ACIDS,ALKALI, ALCOHOLS	S3,S7	SOAP	F1,F7, F9	H1,H5, H9	E2,E9
LEVEL B ---	OXIDIZERS, CHLOROFORMATES	S1,S6, S7	SOAP	F1,F7, F9	H6,H7, H8,H9	E1,E3,E9
LEVEL A ---	OXIDIZERS,AIR	S8,S9	---	F1,F7, F9,F10	H6,H7, H8,H9	E2,E3,E7,E8, E9,E11,E14
LEVEL B VIT(0)	OXIDIZERS, PHOSPHINES	S1,S6, S7,S8	SOAP	F1,F7, F9	H1,H6, H7,H8, H9	E2,E3,E9
LEVEL B ---	OXIDIZERS	S1,S7	SOAP	F2,F7	H9	E1,E3
LEVEL A VIN(+)	ALCOHOLS, ACIDS, AMINES,HEAT,STEEL, OXIDIZERS	S1,S6, S7,S8	DRY	F1,F7, F9	H5,H6, H7,H8, H9,H10	E2,E3,E6
LEVEL A ---	OXIDIZERS,WATER	S1,S7	SOAP	F2,F7, F9	H5,H6, H7,H8, H9	E2,E3,E4, E9
LEVEL B ---	HgO,OXIDIZERS	S2,S5, S6,S8	---	F1,F7, F9	H6,H7, H8,H9	E1,E3,E4, E9
LEVEL A VIN(+) TEF(0)	AMINES,OXIDIZERS, HALOGENS	S1,S6, S7,S8	SOAP	F1,F7, F9	H1,H5, H9	E1,E3,E4, E6,E9
LEVEL B ---	OXIDIZERS	S1,S7	WATER	F1,F7, F9	H6,H7, H8,H9	E1,E3,E9
LEVEL A ---	OXIDIZERS	S3,S7, S8	ALK. HYPO- CHLOR.	F1,F7, F9	H9,H14	E2,E9
LEVEL B ---	OXIDIZERS	S1,S6, S7	SOAP	F2,F7	H9	E1,E3,E4
LEVEL A ---	OXIDIZERS,WATER	S3,S7	FLOOD. WATER	F3,F7, F9,F14	H6,H7, H8,H9	E2,E7,E9,E12

CHEMICAL NAME	DOT #	CAS #	FORM	NFPA	VAPOR PRESS.	WATER SOL.
N-METHYL-PIPERIDINE	2399	626-67-5	C. LIQ. < 1	---	---	S.
METHYL PROPIONATE	1248	554-12-1	C. LIQ. < 1	---	MOD.	0%
2-METHYL-TETRAHYDROFURAN	2536	96-47-9	C. LIQ. < 1	2-3-0	HIGH	< 1%
METHYL TRICHLOROSILANE	1250	75-79-6	C. LIQ. > 1	3-3-2 W	HIGH	DEC.
METHYL VINYL KETONE	1251	78-94-4	C. LIQ. < 1	3-3-2	HIGH	0%
MEVINPHOS® ***	2783	7786-34-7	YELL. LIQ. > 1	---	---	S.
MORPHOLINE	1760 2054	110-91-8	C. LIQ. < 1	2-3-0	MOD.	S.
NAPHTHA	1255 1256 2553	8030-30-6	C. LIQ. < 1	1-3-0	HIGH	0%
NAPHTHALENE ***	1334 2304	91-20-3	WHITE POWD.	2-2-0	LOW	0%
1-NAPHTHYLAMINE ***	2077	134-32-7	TAN POWD.	2-1-0	LOW	< 1%
1-NAPHTHYL-THIOUREA ***	1651	86-88-4	GREY POWD.	---	LOW	0%
NICKEL CARBONYL ***	1259	13463-39-3	WHITE POWD.	4-3-3	HIGH	0%
NICKEL NITRATE	2725	13138-45-9	GREEN POWD.	---	---	S.
NICOTINE ***	1654	54-11-5	C. LIQ. 1.0	4-1-0	LOW	S.

PPE	INCOMPATIBILITIES	SPILL	DECON.	FIRE	FIRST AID	SPECIAL
LEVEL B ---	OXIDIZERS	S1,S7	WATER	F2,F7	H9	E1,E3,E4
LEVEL B ---	OXIDIZERS	S1,S6, S7	SOAP	F2,F7	H9	E1,E3,E4
LEVEL B ---	OXIDIZERS	S1,S6, S7	SOAP	F2,F7	H9	E1,E3,E4, E5
LEVEL A ---	ALCOHOLS,WATER	S1,S7	BASE	F2,F7, F9	H6,H7, H8,H9	E2,E3,E4,E7, E12
LEVEL A ---	ALKALI,OXIDIZERS, LIGHT, REDUCING AGENTS	S1,S6, S7	SOAP	F2,F7, F9,F10	H6,H7, H8,H9	E2,E3,E4, E6,E14
LEVEL A ---	OXIDIZERS	S1,S7	SOAP	F1,F7, F9	H9,H14	E2,E9
LEVEL B BUT(+) VIN(0)	ACIDS,OXIDIZERS	S1,S6, S7	WATER	F1,F7, F9	H6,H7, H8,H9	E1,E3,E9
LEVEL B NIT(+) VIN(0) VIT(0)	OXIDIZERS	S1,S6, S7	SOAP	F1,F7	H9	E1,E3
LEVEL B TEF(+)	OXIDIZERS	S3,S8	SOAP	F1,F7	H9,H12	E1,E17
LEVEL B ---	OXIDIZERS	S3,S8	SOAP	F1,F7, F9	H2,H9, H12	E2,E9
LEVEL A ---	OXIDIZERS	S3,S8	SOAP	F1,F7, F9	H1,H9	E2
LEVEL A ---	AIR,HALOGENS, OXIDIZERS, COMBUSTIBLES	S8,S9	---	F1,F7, F9	H2,H6, H9,H12	E2,E3,E4,E8, E9
LEVEL B ---	COMBUSTIBLES, REDUCING AGENTS, POWDERED METALS	S3,S7	WATER	F4,F7	H1,H9	E1,E13
LEVEL A ---	OXIDIZERS	S1,S7, S8	WATER	F1,F7, F9	H9,H12	E2,E9

CHEMICAL NAME	DOT #	CAS #	FORM	NFPA	VAPOR PRESS.	WATER SOL.
NITRIC ACID ***	1760 2031	7697-37-2	C. LIQ. > 1	3-0-0 OX	MOD.	S.
NITRIC ACID, FUMING ***	2032	7697-37-2	RED LIQ. > 1	3-0-1 OX	HIGH	S.
NITRIC OXIDE ***	1660	10102-43-9	C. GAS	---	GAS	DEC.
p-NITROANILINE ***	1661	100-01-6	YELL. POWD.	3-1-2	LOW	0%
NITROBENZENE ***	1662	98-95-3	YELL. LIQ. > 1	3-2-1	LOW	< 1%
NITROBENZO- TRIFLUORIDE	2306	98-46-4	YELL. POWD.	---	LOW	0%
NITROETHANE	2842	79-24-3	C. LIQ. > 1	1-3-3	MOD.	0%
NITROGEN DIOXIDE ***	1067	10102-44-0	RED GAS	3-3-0 OX	GAS	---
NITROGEN TRIFLUORIDE ***	2451	7783-54-2	C. GAS	---	GAS	DEC.
NITROGUANIDINE	0282 1336	556-88-7	WHITE POWD.	---	LOW	4%
p-NITROPHENOL ***	1663	100-02-7	YELL. POWD.	---	LOW	0%
NITROPROPANE ***	2608	108-03-2	C. LIQ. 1.0	1-3-2	MOD.	0%
NITROSYL CHLORIDE ***	1069	2696-92-6	YELL. GAS	---	GAS	DEC.
o-NITROTOLUENE	1664	88-72-2	YELL. LIQ. > 1	3-1-1	LOW	0%

PPE	INCOMPATIBILITIES	SPILL	DECON.	FIRE	FIRST AID	SPECIAL
LEVEL B BUT(+) SAR(+)	COMBUSTIBLES, SULFIDES, CARBIDES, POWDERED METALS	S3,S7	BASE	F1,F7, F9,F14	H6,H7, H8,H9	E2,E9, E13
LEVEL B BUT(+) SAR(+)	COMBUSTIBLES, SULFIDES, CARBIDES, POWDERED METALS	S3,S7	BASE	F1,F7, F9,F14	H6,H7, H8,H9	E2,E9,E13, E16
LEVEL B ---	COMBUSTIBLES,O_3,NH_3, HALOGENS,METALS, HALOCARBONS	S5,S6, S8	---	F4,F7, F9	H6,H7, H8,H9	E2,E7,E9
LEVEL B ---	OXIDIZERS, REDUCING AGENTS, ACIDS	S3,S7, S8	SOAP	F1,F7, F9	H9,H12	E2,E9
LEVEL B BUT(+) VIT(+) TEF(0)	OXIDIZERS,$AlCl_3$, ACIDS,ANILINE	S1,S7, S8	SOAP	F1,F7, F9,F10	H9,H12	E2,E9,E13, E14
LEVEL B ---	OXIDIZERS, BASES, REDUCING AGENTS	S1,S7	SOAP	F1,F7, F9	H9	E1,E9
LEVEL B BUT(+)	OXIDIZERS,ACIDS, METAL OXIDES,BASES, AMINES	S1,S6, S7	SOAP	F2,F7, F9,F10	H9,H12	E2,E3,E8,E9, E13,E14
LEVEL A SAR(+)	COMBUSTIBLES, HALOCARBONS	S2,S5, S6,S8	---	F4,F7, F9,F10	H6,H7, H8,H9, H12	E2,E3,E9, E13
LEVEL A ---	REDUCING AGENTS, COMBUSTIBLES,H_2, WATER,H_2S,NH_3,CO	S2, S5,S6	---	F1,F7, F9,F10	H6,H7, H8,H9, H12	E2,E3,E9
LEVEL B	OXIDIZERS	S3,S7	SOAP	F4,F7, F9,F10	H9	E1,E8,E9, E14
LEVEL B ---	OXIDIZERS	S3,S7, S8	SOAP	F1,F7, F9	H8,H9, H12	E1,E9
LEVEL B BUT(+) VIN(+) TEF(0)	OXIDIZERS,BASES, METAL OXIDES,	S1,S6, S7,S8	SOAP	F2,F7, F9,F10	H9	E1,E3,E8, E9,E13,E14
LEVEL B ---	H_2,O_2,Pt, COMBUSTIBLES	S5,S6	---	F1,F7, F9,F10	H6,H7, H8,H9	E2,E7,E9
LEVEL B ---	OXIDIZERS, BASES	S1,S7	SOAP	F1,F7, F9,F10	H9,H12	E2,E8,E9, E14

CHEMICAL NAME	DOT #	CAS #	FORM	NFPA	VAPOR PRESS.	WATER SOL.
NITROUS OXIDE	1070 2201	10024-97-2	C. GAS	---	GAS	3%
OCTANE	1262	111-65-9	C. LIQ. < 1	0-3-0	MOD.	0%
tert-OCTYL MERCAPTAN ***	3023	63834-87-7	C. LIQ. < 1	2-2-0	---	0%
OSMIUM TETROXIDE ***	2471	20816-12-0	YELL. POWD.	---	MOD.	6%
OXALIC ACID	2449	144-62-7	WHITE POWD.	2-1-0	LOW	14%
OXYGEN	1072 1073	7782-44-7	C. GAS	---	GAS	14%
PARA-FORMALDEHYDE	2213	30525-89-4	WHITE POWD.	2-1-0	LOW	DEC.
PARALDEHYDE ***	1264	123-63-7	C. LIQ. 1.0	2-3-1	---	S.
PARAQUAT®	2588	1910-42-5	YELL. POWD.	---	LOW	S.
PARATHION® ***	2783	56-38-2	YELL. LIQ. > 1	---	LOW	0%
PENTABORANE ***	1380	19624-22-7	C. LIQ. < 1	4-4-2	HIGH	DEC.
PENTACHLORO-ETHANE ***	1669	76-01-7	C. LIQ. > 1	---	MOD.	0%
PERCHLORIC ACID	1802 1873	7601-90-3	C. LIQ. > 1	---	HIGH	S.
PERCHLORO-ETHYLENE ***	1897	127-18-4	C. LIQ. > 1	2-0-0	MOD.	0%

PPE	INCOMPATIBILITIES	SPILL	DECON.	FIRE	FIRST AID	SPECIAL
LEVEL B ---	Al,B,NH₃,H₂,CO,H₂S, REDUCING AGENTS, PHOSPHINE,CARBIDES	S5,S6	---	F1,F7	H11	E1
LEVEL B NIT(0) VIT(0)	OXIDIZERS	S1,S6, S7	SOAP	F1,F7	H9	E1,E3
LEVEL B ---	OXIDIZERS	S1,S7	SOAP	F1,F7, F9	H9	E1,E3,E9
LEVEL B ---	REDUCING AGENTS	S8,S9	WATER	F1,F7, F9	H8,H9, H15	E2
LEVEL B BUT(+) VIT(+) NEO(+)	Ag,OXIDIZERS, FURFURYL ALCOHOL	S3,S7	WATER	F1,F7, F9	H6,H8, H9	E1
LEVEL B ---	COMBUSTIBLES, OXIDIZABLE MATERIALS	S5,S6	---	F6,F7	H9,H13	E1,E13,E16
LEVEL B BUT(-)	OXIDIZERS,Cu and ALLOYS, OXIDES, ISOCYANATES	S3,S7	WATER	F2,F7, F9	H5,H6, H7, H8,H9	E1
LEVEL B ---	OXIDIZERS,IODIDES, ALKALI,CYANIDES	S1,S7, S9	WATER	F2,F7, F9	H9	E1,E3
LEVEL A ---	OXIDIZERS	S3,S7	WATER	F1,F7, F9	H6,H9	E2,E9
LEVEL A TEF(0)	OXIDIZERS, ENDRIN®	S1,S7, S8	SOAP	F1,F7, F9	H9,H14	E2,E9
LEVEL A ---	OXIDIZERS,WATER, HALOCARBONS, ETHERS,ESTERS	S9	---	F7,F12	H6,H7, H8,H9	E2,E3,E7,E8, E9,E11,E16
LEVEL A ---	OXIDIZERS, ALKALI METALS	S1,S6, S7,S8	SOAP	F1,F7, F9	H1,H9	E1,E9
LEVEL B RUB(+) NEO(+) NIT(+) VIN(+)	ALCOHOLS,AMINES, COMBUSTIBLES, KETONES,HALIDES, ANHYDRIDES, ORGANOPHOSPHATES	S3,S7	WATER	F4,F7, F9	H8,H9	E1,E7,E9, E13,E16
LEVEL B VIT(+) TEF(+) VIN(+)	Be,Ba,ALKALI METALS, ALKALI	S1,S6, S7,S8	SOAP	F6,F7, F9	H9	E1,E9

CHEMICAL NAME	DOT #	CAS #	FORM	NFPA	VAPOR PRESS.	WATER SOL.
PERCHLOROMETHYL MERCAPTAN ***	1670	594-42-3	YELL. LIQ. > 1	---	LOW	DEC.
PERCHLORYL FLUORIDE ***	3083	7616-94-6	C. GAS	---	GAS	< 1%
PETROLEUM	1267 1270	8002-05-9	DARK LIQ. > 1	1-3-0	---	0%
PETROLEUM ETHER	1271	64475-85-0	C. LIQ. < 1	1-4-0	HIGH	0%
PHENOL ***	1671 2312 2821	108-95-2	WHITE SOL.	3-2-0	LOW	S.
PHENYLACETO-NITRILE	2470	140-29-4	C. LIQ. 1.0	2-1-0	LOW	0%
1,4-PHENYLENE-DIAMINE	1673	106-50-3	WHITE POWD.	---	LOW	5%
PHENYL-HYDRAZINE	2572	100-63-0	YELL. LIQ. > 1	3-2-0	LOW	< 1%
PHENYL ISOCYANATE ***	2487	103-71-9	C. LIQ. > 1	---	LOW	DEC.
PHENYL MERCAPTAN ***	2337	108-98-5	C. LIQ. > 1	---	LOW	S.
PHOSGENE ***	1076	75-44-5	C. GAS	4-0-1	GAS	< 1%
PHOSPHINE ***	2199	7803-51-2	C. GAS	3-4-2	GAS	0%
PHOSPHORIC ACID	1805	7664-38-2	C. LIQ. > 1	3-0-0	LOW	S.
PHOSPHORUS (RED) ***	1338	7723-14-0	RED SOL.	1-1-1	LOW	0%

PPE	INCOMPATIBILITIES	SPILL	DECON.	FIRE	FIRST AID	SPECIAL
LEVEL A ---	ALKALI, AMINES, WATER, OXIDIZERS	S3,S7, S8	DRY	F6,F7, F9	H6,H7, H8,H9	E2,E7,E9,E12
LEVEL A ---	COMBUSTIBLES, POWDERED METALS, REDUCING AGENTS, AMINES, BASES	S5,S6	---	F4,F7, F9	H6,H7, H8,H9, H12	E2,E7,E9,E16
LEVEL B ---	OXIDIZERS	S1,S7	SOAP	F1,F7, F9	H1,H9	E1,E3,E9
LEVEL B NIT(0) TEF(0)	OXIDIZERS	S1,S6, S7	SOAP	F2,F7	H6,H9	E1,E3
LEVEL A BUT(+) VIT(+)	OXIDIZERS, AlCL3, BUTADIENE, FORMALDEHYDE	S3,S7, S8	WATER	F1,F7, F9	H6,H7, H8,H9	E2,E9,E17
LEVEL A ---	OXIDIZERS	S1,S7	SOAP	F1,F7, F9	H9	E2,E9
LEVEL B ---	OXIDIZERS	S3	SOAP	F1,F7, F9	H1,H9, H12	E2,E9
LEVEL A ---	OXIDIZERS, PbO2	S1,S7	SOAP	F1,F7, F9	H2,H6 H7,H8, H9	E2,E9,E16
LEVEL B ---	OXIDIZERS, AMINES, ALCOHOLS, WATER	S1,S7	FLOOD WATER	F1,F7, F9	H5,H6, H9	E2,E3,E9
LEVEL B ---	OXIDIZERS	S1,S7, S8	WATER	F1,F7, F9,F10	H6,H7, H8,H9	E2,E3,E9
LEVEL A ---	Al,NH3,ALCOHOLS, ALKALI, AZIDES	S5,S6, S8	---	F1,F7, F9	H6,H7, H8,H9	E2,E3,E9
LEVEL A ---	OXIDIZERS, AIR, NITRATES, HALOGENS, NITROGEN OXIDES	S5,S6, S8	---	F1,F7, F9,F10	H6,H7, H8,H9	E2,E3,E4,E9
LEVEL B RUB(+) NEO(+) NIT(+) VIN(+)	POWDERED METALS, STAINLESS STEEL, CHLORIDES, ALKALI	S3,S7	WATER	F6,F7	H6,H7, H8,H9	E1,E7,E12, E16
LEVEL B ---	OXIDIZERS, OXIDES, HALIDES, SULFATES, Cu and ALLOYS, S	S3,S7	DRY	F1,F7	H6,H7, H8,H9	E2,E9

CHEMICAL NAME	DOT #	CAS #	FORM	NFPA	VAPOR PRESS.	WATER SOL.
PHOSPHORUS (WHITE or YELLOW) ***	1381 2447	7723-14-0	WHITE SOL.	3-4-2	LOW	0%
PHOSPHORUS OXYCHLORIDE ***	1810	10025-87-3	C. LIQ. > 1	3-0-2 W̶	MOD.	DEC.
PHOSPHORUS PENTACHLORIDE	1806	10026-13-8	YELL. POWD.	3-0-2 W̶	LOW	DEC.
PHOSPHORUS PENTASULFIDE ***	1340	1314-80-3	YELL. POWD.	---	LOW	DEC.
PHOSPHORUS PENTOXIDE	1807	1314-56-3	WHITE POWD.	---	LOW	DEC.
PHOSPHORUS TRICHLORIDE ***	1809	7719-12-2	C. LIQ. > 1	3-0-2 W̶	HIGH	DEC.
PHTHALIC ANHYDRIDE ***	2214	85-44-9	WHITE POWD.	2-1-0	LOW	DEC.
3-PICOLINE	2313	108-99-6	C. LIQ < 1	2-2-0	LOW	S.
PICRIC ACID	1344 1336	88-89-1	YELL. POWD.	3-4-4	LOW	0%
PINDONE	2472	83-26-1	YELL. POWD.	---	LOW	0%
2-PINENE	2368	80-56-8	C. LIQ. < 1	1-3-0	MOD.	0%
PIPERAZINE	2579	110-85-0	WHITE POWD.	2-2-0	---	S.
PIPERIDINE	2401	110-89-4	C. LIQ. < 1	2-3-3	MOD.	S.
POTASSIUM	1420 2257	7440-09-7	SILV METAL	3-3-2 W̶	LOW	DEC.

PPE	INCOMPATIBILITIES	SPILL	DECON.	FIRE	FIRST AID	SPECIAL
LEVEL A ---	BASES,AIR,S,METALS, OXIDIZERS,HALIDES, HALOGENS	S9	---	F5,F7, F9	H8,H9	E2,E7,E9, E11,E16
LEVEL A TRF(0)	WATER,ACIDS, ALCOHOLS,ALKALI, ALKALI METALS	S9	---	F1,F7, F9	H6,H7, H8,H9	E2,E7,E9, E11,E12,E16
LEVEL A ---	OXIDIZERS,WATER, HALOGENS,METALS, COMBUSTIBLES	S9	---	F1,F7, F9	H6,H7, H8,H9	E2,E7,E9, E11,E12,E16
LEVEL B ---	OXIDIZERS,WATER, COMBUSTIBLES, ALKALI METALS	S8,S9	---	F5,F7, F9,F13	H6,H7, H8,H9	E2,E7,E9, E12,E16
LEVEL A ---	REACTS WITH NUMEROUS CLASSES OF MATERIALS	S9	---	F5,F7, F9	H6,H7, H8,H9	E2,E7,E9, E11,E12,E16
LEVEL B TEF(-)	REACTS WITH NUMEROUS CLASSES OF MATERIALS	S9	---	F5,F7, F9,F13	H6,H7, H8,H9	E2,E7,E9, E12,E16
LEVEL B ---	OXIDIZERS,ACIDS, NITRATES,OXIDES	S3,S7, S8	BASE	F1,F7, F9	H5,H9	E1,E12
LEVEL B ---	OXIDIZERS	S1,S7	SOAP	F1,F7, F9	H6,H7, H8,H9	E1,E3,E9
LEVEL B ---	CONCRETE,Ca,Al,NH₃, POWDERED METALS, AMINES,REDUCING AGENTS	S9	---	F4,F7, F9,F10 F14	H9	E1,E8,E9, E13
LEVEL B ---	OXIDIZERS	S3,S7	SOAP	F6,F7, F9	H9	E1,E9
LEVEL B ---	OXIDIZERS	S1,S6, S7	SOAP	F2,F7, F9	H8,H9	E1,E3,E9
LEVEL B ---	OXIDIZERS	S3,S7	SOAP	F2,F7, F9	H6,H7, H8,H9	E1,E9
LEVEL B ---	OXIDIZERS	S1,S6, S7	WATER	F1,F7, F9	H6,H7, H8,H9	E2,E3,E9
LEVEL B ---	AIR,WATER,CO,CO₂, HALOCARBONS, OXIDIZERS	S9	---	F5,F7, F13	H8,H9	E2,E5,E7, E12,E16

CHEMICAL NAME	DOT #	CAS #	FORM	NFPA	VAPOR PRESS.	WATER SOL.
POTASSIUM BROMATE	1484	7758-01-2	WHITE POWD.	---	LOW	S.
POTASSIUM CHLORATE	1485 2427	3811-04-9	WHITE POWD.	1-0-1 OX	LOW	---
POTASSIUM CYANIDE ***	1680	151-50-8	WHITE POWD.	3-0-0	LOW	S.
POTASSIUM DICHLORO-ISOCYANURATE	2465	2244-21-5	WHITE POWD.	3-0-2 OX	LOW	DEC.
POTASSIUM DICHROMATE	1479	7778-50-9	ORANG. POWD.	---	LOW	S.
POTASSIUM HYDROGEN FLUORIDE	1811	7789-29-9	WHITE POWD.	---	NONE	S.
POTASSIUM HYDROXIDE	1813	1310-58-3	WHITE POWD.	3-0-1	NONE	S.
POTASSIUM PERMANGANATE ***	1490	7722-64-7	PURPLE POWD.	---	LOW	S.
POTASSIUM PERSULFATE	1492	7727-21-1	WHITE POWD.	---	LOW	S.
POTASSIUM SULFIDE	1382 1847	1312-73-8	WHITE POWD.	3-1-0	LOW	S.
PROPANE	1978	74-98-6	C. GAS	1-4-0	GAS	0%
PROPANETHIOL	2402	107-03-0	C. LIQ. < 1	---	HIGH	S.
PROPARGYL ALCOHOL ***	1986	107-19-7	C. LIQ. 1.0	3-3-3	MOD.	S.
PROPIONALDEHYDE	1275	123-38-6	C. LIQ. < 1	2-3-2	HIGH	20%
PROPIONIC ACID ***	1848	79-09-4	C. LIQ. 1.0	2-2-0	LOW	S.

PPE	INCOMPATIBILITIES	SPILL	DECON.	FIRE	FIRST AID	SPECIAL
LEVEL B ---	COMBUSTIBLES,S,Al, SULFIDES,P,As,C,Se, REDUCING AGENTS	S3,S7	WATER	F4,F7	H8,H9	E1,E7,E13, E16
LEVEL B ---	COMBUSTIBLES,S,Al, SULFIDES,P,As,C,Se, REDUCING AGENTS	S3,S7	WATER	F4,F7	H8,H9	E1,E7,E13, E16
LEVEL A RUB(-) NEO(-) NIT(-)	ACIDS,OXIDIZERS	S3,S7, S8	ALK. HYPO- CHLOR.	F1,F7, F9	H9,H10	E2,E7,E9, E16
LEVEL B ---	NH₃,AMMONIUM SALTS,WATER, REDUCING AGENTS	S3,S7	FLOOD. WATER	F4,F7, F9	H6,H7, H8,H9	E1,E7,E9, E16
LEVEL B ---	COMBUSTIBLES, REDUCING AGENTS	S3,S7	FLOOD. WATER	F4,F7, F9	H2,H6, H7,H8, H9	E2,E7,E9,E13
LEVEL A ---	ACIDS	S3,S7	WATER	F1,F7, F9	H6,H7, H8,H9	E2,E7,E9
LEVEL B NEO(+) VIN(+)	OXIDIZERS,Al,Sn, ACIDS,Pb,Zn, HALOGENS	S3,S7	WATER	F6,F7	H6,H7, H8,H9	E1,E7,E12, E16
LEVEL B ---	REACTS WITH NUMEROUS CHEMICAL CLASSES	S3,S7	WATER	F4,F7, F9	H6,H7, H8,H9	E1,E7,E8,E9, E13,E16
LEVEL B ---	POWDERED METALS, REDUCING AGENTS, BASES,HYDRAZINE	S3,S7	WATER	F4,F7, F9	H5,H9	E1,E7,E9
LEVEL B ---	ACIDS,WATER, NITRIC OXIDE	S3,S7	BASE	F1,F7, F9	H6,H7, H8,H9	E1,E7,E9, E16
LEVEL B ---	OXIDIZERS	S5,S6	---	F1,F7	H9,H13	E1,E3
LEVEL B ---	OXIDIZERS, ALKALI METALS	S1,S6, S7	WATER	F1,F7	H9	E1,E3,E4,E9
LEVEL A ---	OXIDIZERS,ALKALI, ACIDS,P₂O₃	S1,S6, S7,S8	WATER	F2,F7, F9,F10	H8,H9	E2,E3,E6,E9, E14
LEVEL B BUT(+)	OXIDIZERS, METHYL METHACRYLATE	S1,S6, S7	WATER	F2,F7, F9	H6,H7, H8,H9	E2,E3,E4,E9
LEVEL B TEF(0)	OXIDIZERS	S1,S7	WATER	F2,F7	H6,H7, H8,H9	E1,E3

CHEMICAL NAME	DOT #	CAS #	FORM	NFPA	VAPOR PRESS.	WATER SOL.
PROPIONIC ANHYDRIDE ***	2496	123-62-6	C. LIQ. 1.0	2-2-1	MOD.	DEC.
PROPIONITRILE ***	2404	107-12-0	C. LIQ. < 1	4-3-1	MOD.	10%
PROPIONYL CHLORIDE	1815	79-03-8	C. LIQ. > 1	3-3-1	---	DEC.
n-PROPYL CHLOROFORMATE	2740	109-61-5	C. LIQ. > 1	---	MOD.	DEC
PROPYLENE	1077	115-07-1	C. GAS	1-4-1	GAS	0%
PROPYLENE DICHLORIDE ***	1279	78-87-5	C. LIQ. > 1	2-3-0	MOD.	0%
PROPYLENE IMINE ***	1921	75-55-8	C. LIQ. < 1	---	HIGH	DEC.
PROPYLENE OXIDE ***	1280	75-56-9	C. LIQ. < 1	4-2-2	HIGH	S.
PROPYLTRICHLORO-SILANE	1816	141-57-1	C. LIQ. > 1	3-3-1	---	DEC.
PYRIDINE ***	1282	110-86-1	C. LIQ. 1.0	2-3-0	MOD.	S.
QUINOLINE ***	2656	91-22-5	C. LIQ. > 1	2-1-0	LOW	0%
RESORCINOL ***	2876	108-46-3	WHITE POWD.	---	LOW	S.
RUBIDIUM	1423	7440-17-7	SILV. METAL	---	LOW	DEC.
RUBIDIUM HYDROXIDE	2677 2678	1310-82-3	WHITE POWD.	---	LOW	S.

PPE	INCOMPATIBILITIES	SPILL	DECON.	FIRE	FIRST AID	SPECIAL
LEVEL B ---	OXIDIZERS	S1,S6, S7	BASE	F1,F7	H6,H7, H8,H9	E1,E3
LEVEL A VIN(+)	OXIDIZERS,ACIDS	S1,S6, S7,S8	ALK. HYPO-CHLOR.	F2,F7, F9	H9,H10	E2,E3,E7, E9
LEVEL B ---	WATER,ALCOHOLS, ETHERS	S1,S7	BASE	F2,F7, F9	H6,H7, H8,H9	E2,E3,E7,E9
LEVEL A ---	OXIDIZERS,WATER, ACIDS	S1,S6, S7	BASE	F1,F7, F9	H6,H7, H8,H9	E2,E3,E7, E9,E12
LEVEL C ---	OXIDIZERS, NITROGEN OXIDES, SULFUR DIOXIDE	S2,S5, S6	---	F1,F7	H1,H9, H13	E1,E3,E4,E6
LEVEL A ---	OXIDIZERS,Al and ALLOYS	S1,S6, S7,S8	SOAP	F1,F7	H1,H9	E1,E3,E4,E9
LEVEL A ---	OXIDIZERS,ACIDS, WATER	S1,S6, S7,S8	BASE	F1,F7, F9	H2,H6, H7, H8,H9	E2,E3,E6,E9
LEVEL A ---	OXIDIZERS,ACIDS, AMMONIUM HYDROXIDE	S1,S6, S7	WATER	F2,F7, F9	H2,H8, H9	E2,E3,E4,E16
LEVEL B ---	OXIDIZERS,WATER	S1,S6, S7	BASE	F1,F7, F9	H6,H7, H8,H9	E1,E3,E7,E9
LEVEL B BUT(+)	OXIDIZERS,ACIDS	S1,S6, S7,S8	WATER	F2,F7, F9	H9	E1,E3,E9
LEVEL A ---	OXIDIZERS	S1,S7	SOAP	F2,F7, F9	H1,H9	E1,E9
LEVEL B ---	OXIDIZERS,ACIDS	S1,S7, S8	WATER	F1,F7, F9	H9,H12	E1,E9
LEVEL B ---	WATER,ACIDS,AIR,Hg, OXIDIZERS, HALOCARBONS	S9	DRY	F5,F7, F8	H8,H9	E2,E5,E7, E12,E16
LEVEL B BUT(-) NEO(-)	ACIDS	S3,S7	WATER	F6,F7	H6,H7, H8,H9	E1

CHEMICAL NAME	DOT #	CAS #	FORM	NFPA	VAPOR PRESS.	WATER SOL.
SELENIC ACID	1905	7783-08-6	WHITE POWD.	---	LOW	S.
SELENIUM ***	2658	7782-49-2	GREY METAL	---	LOW	0%
SELENIUM HEXAFLUORIDE ***	2194	7483-79-1	C. GAS	---	GAS	DEC.
SELENIUM OXYCHLORIDE	2879	7791-23-3	C. LIQ. > 1	---	LOW	DEC.
SILANE	2203	7803-62-5	C. GAS	2-4-3	GAS	DEC.
SILICON CHLORIDE	1818	10026-04-7	C. LIQ. > 1	3-0-2 W	HIGH	DEC.
*** SILICON TETRAFLUORIDE	1859	7783-61-1	C. GAS	3-0-2 W	GAS	DEC.
SILVER NITRATE ***	1493	7761-88-8	WHITE POWD.	---	LOW	S.
SODIUM ***	1428 1429	7440-23-5	GREY SOL.	3-3-2 W	LOW	DEC.
SODIUM AMIDE	1425	7782-92-5	WHITE POWD.	---	---	DEC.
SODIUM AZIDE ***	1687	26628-22-8	WHITE POWD.	---	LOW	S.
SODIUM BISULFATE	1821 2693 2837	7631-90-5	WHITE POWD.	---	LOW	S.
SODIUM BOROHYDRIDE	1426	16940-66-2	WHITE POWD.	---	LOW	DEC.
SODIUM CACODYLATE	1688	124-65-2	WHITE POWD.	---	LOW	S.

PPE	INCOMPATIBILITIES	SPILL	DECON.	FIRE	FIRST AID	SPECIAL
LEVEL B ---	ALKALI	S3,S7	WATER	F6,F7, F9	H1,H8, H9	E1,E9
LEVEL B	ACIDS,CARBIDES,Ni,Zn, OXIDIZERS,U, HALOGENS	S3,S7	SOAP	F1,F7, F9	H9	E1,E9
LEVEL A ---	OXIDIZERS, SILVER OXIDE	S5,S6		F1,F7, F9	H6,H9	E2,E7,E9
LEVEL A ---	METAL OXIDES,Sb, K,P	S1,S7	WATER	F1,F7, F9	H6,H7, H8,H9	E2,E7,E9
LEVEL B ---	OXIDIZERS,AIR,O$_2$, HALOGENS, CHLORIDES	S2,S5, S6	---	F1,F7, F9	H9	E1,E3,E4, E11
LEVEL B ---	WATER,ALKALI METALS,DIMETHYL SULFOXIDE	S1,S6, S7	DRY	F3,F7, F8,F9	H6,H7, H8,H9	E1,E7,E9,E12
LEVEL A ---	WATER	S5,S6	---	F1,F7, F9	H6,H7, H8,H9	E2,E7,E9,E12
LEVEL B ---	REDUCING AGENTS,P, NH$_3$,PH$_3$,ALKALI, ALKENES,ALKYNES	S3,S7	WATER	F4,F7	H6,H7, H8,H9	E2,E13
LEVEL B ---	WATER,OXIDIZERS, HALOCARBONS, METAL OXIDES	S9	---	F5,F7, F8	H6,H7, H8,H9	E2,E12,E16
LEVEL B ---	OXIDIZERS,WATER, HALOCARBONS, HALOGENS	S9	---	F5,F7, F8,F9	H8,H9	E2,E7,E9, E10,E12,E15
LEVEL A ---	ACIDS,ALKALI,CS$_2$, METALS,HALIDES, HALOGENS, HYDRAZINE	S3,S7, S8	WATER	F1,F7, F9	H1,H9	E2,E8,E9, E14,E16
LEVEL B ---	ACIDS,OXIDIZERS	S3,S7	WATER	F1,F7	H6,H7, H8,H9	E1
LEVEL B ---	ALKALI,WATER,ACIDS, POWDERED METALS, OXIDIZERS,ALCOHOLS, METAL SALTS	S3,S7	FLOOD. WATER	F1,F7	H6,H7, H8,H9	E1,E7,E16
LEVEL A ---	ACIDS,OXIDIZERS	S3,S7	WATER	F1,F7, F9	H2,H9	E2,E9

CHEMICAL NAME	DOT #	CAS #	FORM	NFPA	VAPOR PRESS.	WATER SOL.
SODIUM CHLORITE	1496 1908	7758-19-2	WHITE POWD.	---	LOW	S.
SODIUM CYANIDE ***	1689	143-33-9	WHITE POWD.	---	LOW	S.
SODIUM FLUORIDE ***	1690	7681-49-4	WHITE POWD.	2-0-0	LOW	S.
SODIUM FLUOROACETATE	2629	62-74-8	WHITE POWD.	---	LOW	S.
SODIUM HYDRIDE	1427	7646-69-7	GREY POWD.	3-3-2 W	LOW	DEC.
SODIUM HYDROSULFIDE ***	2318 2922 2923 2949	16721-80-5	YELL. POWD.	---	LOW	S.
SODIUM HYDROSULFITE	1384	7775-14-6	WHITE POWD.	3-1-2	LOW	S.
SODIUM HYDROXIDE ***	1823 1824	1310-73-2	WHITE POWD.	3-0-1	LOW	S.
SODIUM HYPOCHLORITE	1791	7681-52-9	C. LIQ. > 1	---	---	S.
SODIUM METHYLATE (DRY) ***	1431	124-41-4	WHITE POWD.	---	HIGH	DEC.
SODIUM METHYLATE (SOLUTION) ***	1289	124-41-4	C. LIQ. < 1	---	HIGH	DEC.
SODIUM MONOXIDE	1825	1313-59-3	WHITE POWD.	---	LOW	DEC.
SODIUM NITRATE	1498	7631-99-4	WHITE POWD.	---	LOW	S.
SODIUM NITRITE ***	1500	7632-00-0	WHITE POWD.	---	LOW	S.

PPE	INCOMPATIBILITIES	SPILL	DECON.	FIRE	FIRST AID	SPECIAL
LEVEL B ---	COMBUSTIBLES,S,Zn, REDUCING AGENTS, P,ACIDS,NH₃	S3,S7	WATER	F4,F7, F9	H9,H12	E1,E7,E9,E13
LEVEL A ---	ACIDS,OXIDIZERS	S3,S7, S8	ALK. HYPO-CHLOR.	F6,F7, F9	H9,H10	E2,E7,E9, E16
LEVEL B RUB(+) NEO(+) NIT(+) VIN(+)	ACID	S3,S7	WATER	F6,F7, F9	H9	E1,E7,E9
LEVEL A ---	ACIDS,OXIDIZERS	S3,S7	WATER	F6,F7, F9	H9	E2,E7,E9
LEVEL B ---	WATER,HALOGENS,S, ALCOHOLS,DMF, ACETYLENE	S9	---	F5,F7, F9	H8,H9	E1,E7,E9, E10, E12,E16
LEVEL A ---	AIR,OXIDIZERS,Zn and ALLOYS,Al,Cu, DIAZONIUM SALTS	S1,S7	WATER	F6,F7, F9,F10	H6,H7, H8,H9	E2,E7,E9, E11,E16
LEVEL B ---	OXIDIZERS,WATER	S1,S7	WATER	F4,F7, F9	H5,H9	E1,E9,E12
LEVEL B NEO(+) VIN(+)	OXIDIZERS,Al,Sn,ACIDS Pb,Zn, HALOGENS	S3,S7	WATER	F6,F7	H6,H7, H8,H9	E1,E7,E12, E16
LEVEL B	COMBUSTIBLES, AMINES,NITRILES, AMMONIUM SALTS	S3,S7	WATER	F6,F7, F9	H6,H7, H8,H9	E1,E7,E9, E15,E16
LEVEL A ---	ACID,WATER, CHCl₃/ACETONE	S3,S6, S7	SOAP	F5,F7, F9,F10 F12	H6,H7, H8,H9	E2,E7,E9, E10,E12
LEVEL A ---	ACID,WATER, CHCl₃/ACETONE	S3,S7	SOAP	F2,F7, F9,F10 F12	H6,H7, H8,H9	E2,E7,E9, E10,E12,E16
LEVEL A ---	ACIDS,WATER, NITRATED MATERIALS	S3,S7, S9	DRY	F5,F7, F9,F10	H6,H7, H8,H9	E2,E9,E12, E16
LEVEL B ---	COMBUSTIBLES, REDUCING AGENTS, POWDERED METALS	S3,S7	WATER	F4,F7, F9	H9	E1,E13,E14
LEVEL A ---	OXIDIZERS,AMINES, NH₃,IODIDES,Hg SALTS, AMMONIUM SALTS	S3,S7	WATER	F4,F7, F9	H9,H12	E1,E13,E14, E16

CHEMICAL NAME	DOT #	CAS #	FORM	NFPA	VAPOR PRESS.	WATER SOL.
SODIUM PERCHLORATE	1502	7601-89-0	WHITE POWD.	2-0-1 OX	LOW	S.
SODIUM PENTACHLORO-PHENATE	2567	131-52-2	TAN POWD.	---	LOW	S.
SODIUM PEROXIDE	1504	1313-60-6	WHITE POWD.	3-0-1 OX	LOW	S.
SODIUM SELENATE	2630	13410-01-0	WHITE POWD.	---	LOW	S.
SODIUM SELENITE ***	2630	10102-18-8	WHITE POWD.	---	LOW	S.
STANNIC PHOSPHIDE	1433	25324-56-5	SILV. POWD.	---	---	DEC.
STANNOUS CHLORIDE	1759	7772-99-8	WHITE POWD.	---	LOW	S.
STIBINE ***	2676	7803-52-3	C. GAS	4-4-2	GAS	0%
STRYCHNINE ***	1692	57-24-9	WHITE POWD.	---	LOW	0%
STYRENE ***	2055	100-42-5	C. LIQ. < 1	2-3-2	MOD.	0%
SULFAMIC ACID	2967	5329-14-6	WHITE POWD.	---	LOW	S.
SULFUR	1305 2448	7704-34-9	YELL. POWD.	1-1-0	LOW	0%
SULFUR CHLORIDE ***	1828	10025-67-9	YELL. LIQ. > 1	2-1-1	MOD.	DEC.
SULFUR DIOXIDE ***	1079	7446-09-5	C. GAS	3-0-0	GAS	DEC.

PPE	INCOMPATIBILITIES	SPILL	DECON.	FIRE	FIRST AID	SPECIAL
LEVEL B ---	POWDERED METALS, ALCOHOLS, AMINES, REDUCING AGENTS, NITRATES, Mg	S3,S7	WATER	F4,F7, F9	H9	E1,E9,E13, E16
LEVEL A ---	OXIDIZERS	S3,S7	WATER	F1,F7, F9	H9	E2,E9
LEVEL B ---	COMBUSTIBLES,H₂S, POWDERED METALS, ACIDS	S3,S7	WATER	F4,F7, F9,F10	H6,H7, H8,H9	E1,E13,E14, E16
LEVEL A --	ACIDS	S3,S7	WATER	F6,F7, F9	H1,H9	E2,E9
LEVEL A ---	ACIDS	S3,S7	WATER	F6,F7, F9	H9	E2,E9
LEVEL A ---	WATER	S3,S7	DRY	F5,F7, F8,F9, F13	H6,H7, H8,H9	E2,E7,E9, E12,E16
LEVEL B ---	OXIDIZERS,ALKALI METALS,CARBIDES HYDRAZINE	S3,S7	WATER	F6,F7, F9	H6,H7, H8,H9	E1,E9
LEVEL A ---	OXIDIZERS, HALOGENS, AMMONIA	S2,S5, S6	---	F4,F7, F9,F10	H9	E2,E4,E7, E9
LEVEL A ---	OXIDIZERS	S3,S7, S8	SOAP	F6,F7, F9	H5,H9	E2,E9
LEVEL B VIN(0) TEF(0)	OXIDIZERS, AlCl₃, ACIDS,Cu and ALLOYS	S1,S6, S7	SOAP	F1,F7, F9	H9	E1,E3,E6, E9
LEVEL B ---	NH₃,NITRATES, NITRITES,ACIDS	S3,S7	WATER	F6,F7, F9	H9	E1,E9
LEVEL B ---	CARBIDES,P,Pd,Ni,Ca, Al,B,OXIDIZERS,NH₃, HALOGENS, ALKALI METALS	S3,S7	SOAP	F6,F7, F9	H9	E1,E7,E9, E16,E17
LEVEL A ---	OXIDIZERS,WATER, COMBUSTIBLES, METALS	S3,S6, S7	BASE	F1,F7, F8,F9	H6,H7, H8,H9	E2,E7,E9, E12
LEVEL A ---	OXIDIZERS,Al,Cr,Mn, AZIDES,HYDRIDES, POWDERED METALS, HALOGENS,ALKENES	S5,S6	---	F6,F7, F9,F10	H6,H7, H8,H9	E2E7,E9

CHEMICAL NAME	DOT #	CAS #	FORM	NFPA	VAPOR PRESS.	WATER SOL.
SULFURIC ACID ***	1830 1831 1832	7664-93-9	C. LIQ. > 1	3-0-2 W	HIGH	S.
SULFUR TRIOXIDE ***	1829	7446-11-9	WHITE POWD.	---	HIGH	DEC.
SULFUROUS ACID	1833	7782-99-2	C. LIQ. > 1	---	---	S.
SULFURYL CHLORIDE	1834	7791-25-5	C. LIQ. > 1	3-0-1	HIGH	DEC.
SULFURYL FLUORIDE ***	2191	2699-79-8	C. GAS	---	GAS	< 1%
2,4,5-T ***	2765	93-76-5	TAN SOL. ---	---	LOW	< 1%
TELLURIUM HEXAFLUORIDE	2195	7783-80-4	C. GAS	---	GAS	DEC.
TETRACHLORO-ETHANE ***	1702	79-34-5	C. LIQ. > 1	---	MOD.	0%
TETRAETHYLENE-PENTAMINE	2320	112-57-2	C. LIQ. 1.0	2-1-0	LOW	S.
TETRAETHYL LEAD ***	1649	78-00-2	C. LIQ. > 1	3-2-3	LOW	0%
TETRAETHYL PYROPHOSPHATE ***	2783	107-49-3	WHITE LIQ. > 1	---	LOW	S.
TETRAFLUORO-ETHYLENE	1081	116-14-3	C. GAS	2-4-3	GAS	0%
TETRAHYDRO-THIOPHENE	2412	110-01-0	C. LIQ. 1.0	---	---	0%
TETRAMETHYL-AMMONIUM HYDROXIDE	1835	75-59-2	C. LIQ. < 1	---	LOW	S.

PPE	INCOMPATIBILITIES	SPILL	DECON.	FIRE	FIRST AID	SPECIAL
LEVEL B BUT(+) TEF(+) SAR(-)	COMBUSTIBLES,P, CARBIDES,PICRATES, OXIDIZERS, HALOCARBONS	S3,S6, S7	FLOOD. WATER	F6,F7, F9	H6,H7, H8,H9	E2,E9,E12
LEVEL A ---	OXIDIZERS,P, OXIDES,CYANIDES, DMSO	S3,S6, S7	BASE	F6,F7, F9	H6,H7, H8,H9	E2,E7,E9, E12
LEVEL B ---	ALKALI	S3,S7	BASE	F6,F7 F9	H6,H7, H8,H9	E2,E7,E9, E12
LEVEL A ---	COMBUSTIBLES,P,Al NH₃,ALKALI METALS, ALKALI,PbO₂	S3,S6, S7	BASE	F1,F7, F9	H6,H7, H8,H9	E1,E7,E9
LEVEL A ---	ALKALI METALS, Al,AMMONIA	S5,S6	---	F1,F7, F9	H6,H7, H8,H9	E2,E7,E9
LEVEL B ---	OXIDIZERS	S3,S7, S8	SOAP	F1,F7, F9	H9	E1,E9
LEVEL A ---	---	S5,S6	---	F1,F7, F9	H6,H7, H8,H9	E2,E7,E9
LEVEL A VIN(+) VIT(+)	OXIDIZERS, ALKALI METALS	S3,S6, S7,S8	SOAP	F1,F7, F9	H2,H9	E2,E9
LEVEL A BUT(+) NEO(+) VIT(+)	OXIDIZERS	S3,S7	WATER	F1,F7, F9	H6,H7, H8,H9	E1,E9
LEVEL B ---	OXIDIZERS	S1,S7, S8	SOAP	F1,F7, F9	H1,H9	E2,E9
LEVEL A ---	WATER,OXIDIZERS	S3,S7, S8	SOAP	F6,F7, F9	H9,H14	E2,E7,E9, E12
LEVEL B BUT(+) NEO(+) VIN(+) VIT(+)	OXIDIZERS,AIR	S2,S5, S6	---	F1,F7, F9	H1,H9	E1,E3,E4, E6,E7,E9, E14
LEVEL B ---	OXIDIZERS	S1,S7	SOAP	F2,F7, F9	H9	E1,E5
LEVEL B ---	OXIDIZERS	S1,S7	WATER	F1,F7, F9	H6,H7, H8,H9	E1,E7,E9

CHEMICAL NAME	DOT #	CAS #	FORM	NFPA	VAPOR PRESS.	WATER SOL.
TETRAMETHYL-METHANEDIAMINE	9069	51-80-9	C. LIQ. < 1	---	---	---
TETRAMETHYL ORTHOSILICATE ***	2606	681-84-5	C. LIQ. 1.0	3-3-1	---	DEC.
TETRAMETHYL-SILANE	2749	75-76-3	C. LIQ. < 1	---	HIGH	DEC.
TETRANITRO-METHANE ***	1510	509-14-8	YELL. LIQ. > 1	---	MOD.	0%
THALLIUM NITRATE ***	2727	10102-45-1	WHITE POWD.	---	LOW	S.
TIN TETRACHLORIDE ***	1827	7646-78-8	C. LIQ. > 1	3-0-1	MOD.	DEC.
TITANIUM	1352 2546 2878	7440-32-6	GREY METAL	---	LOW	0%
TITANIUM TETRACHLORIDE	1838	7550-45-0	C. LIQ. > 1	3-0-2 W	MOD.	DEC.
TITANIUM TRICHLORIDE	2441 2869	7705-07-9	RED POWD.	---	LOW	DEC.
TOLUENE ***	1294	108-88-3	C. LIQ. < 1	2-3-0	MOD.	0%
TOLUENE-2,4-DIAMINE ***	1709	95-80-7	TAN POWD.	---	LOW	S.
TOLUENE-2,4-DIISOCYANATE ***	2078	584-84-9	C. LIQ. > 1	3-1-2	LOW	DEC.
4-TOLUENESULFONIC ACID	2583 2584 2585 2586	104-15-4	WHITE POWD.	---	LOW	S.
o-TOLUIDINE ***	1708	95-53-4	C. LIQ. 1.0	3-2-0	LOW	0%

PPE	INCOMPATIBILITIES	SPILL	DECON.	FIRE	FIRST AID	SPECIAL
LEVEL B ---	OXIDIZERS	S1,S7	SOAP	F1,F7, F9	H9	E1,E3,E4, E9
LEVEL B ---	WATER	S1,S6, S7	WATER	F2,F7, F9	H6,H7, H8,H9	E1,E3,E7,E9, E12
LEVEL A ---	WATER,AIR, OXIDIZERS, HALOGENS	S1,S6, S7	SOAP	F1,F7, F8,F9, F10	H9	E1,E4,E7, E9,E11,E16
LEVEL A ---	Al,OXIDIZERS, AMINES, COMBUSTIBLES	S1,S6, S7,S8	SOAP	F4,F7, F9,F10	H9,H12	E1,E8,E9, E14,E16
LEVEL B ---	REDUCING AGENTS, POWDERED METALS	S3,S7, S8	WATER	F4,F7, F9	H9	E2,E7,E13
LEVEL A ---	COMBUSTIBLES, ALKALI METALS, WATER,NITRATES	S3,S6, S7	BASE	F1,F7, F8,F9	H6,H7, H8,H9	E2,E7,E9, E12,E16
LEVEL B ---	OXIDIZERS, HALOCARBONS, HALOGENS	S3,S7	SOAP	F1,F7	H9	E1
LEVEL A SAR(+)	WATER	S6,S9	---	F3,F7, F8,F9, F14	H6,H7, H8,H9	E2,E7,E9, E12,E16
LEVEL B ---	OXIDIZERS,AIR, ALKALI METALS, WATER	S3,S7	DRY	F3,F7, F8,F9	H6,H7, H8,H9	E2,E7,E9, E12
LEVEL B VIN(+) TEF(+) VIT(+)	OXIDIZERS, NITRIC ACID, NITROMETHANE	S1,S6, S7,S8	SOAP	F1,F7	H6,H9	E1,E3
LEVEL B ---	OXIDIZERS	S3,S7, S8	WATER	F1,F7, F9	H9,H12	E1,E9
LEVEL A BUT(+) VIN(+) NIT(+) VIT(+) SAR(+)	ALKALI,WATER, ALCOHOLS,ACIDS, ACYL CHLORIDES, ORGANOMETALLICS	S3,S7, S8	WATER	F1,F7, F9	H2,H5, H6,H9	E2,E6,E7,E9
LEVEL B NEO(0) VIN(0)	ACETIC ANHYDRIDE, OXIDIZERS	S3,S7	WATER	F1,F7, F9	H9	E1,E9
LEVEL A TEF(0)	OXIDIZERS	S1,S7, S8,S9	SOAP	F1,F7, F9	H2,H9, H12	E2,E9

CHEMICAL NAME	DOT #	CAS #	FORM	NFPA	VAPOR PRESS.	WATER SOL.
TRIBUTYLAMINE ***	2542	102-82-9	C. LIQ. < 1	3-2-0	LOW	0%
TRICHLOROACETIC ACID	1839 2564	76-03-9	WHITE POWD.	---	LOW	S.
TRICHLOROACETYL CHLORIDE	2442	76-02-8	C. LIQ. > 1	---	MOD.	DEC.
1,2,4-TRICHLORO-BENZENE ***	2321	120-82-1	C. LIQ. > 1	2-1-0	LOW	0%
TRICHLORO-ETHYLENE ***	1710	79-01-6	C. LIQ. > 1	2-2-0	HIGH	0%
TRICHLORO-ISOCYANURIC ACID	2468	87-90-1	WHITE POWD.	3-0-2 OX	LOW	DEC.
2,4,6-TRICHLORO-PHENOL ***	2020	88-06-2	WHITE POWD.	---	LOW	S.
TRICHLOROSILANE	1295	10025-78-2	C. LIQ. > 1	3-4-2 W̶	HIGH	DEC.
TRIETHYLAMINE ***	1296	121-44-8	C. LIQ. < 1	2-3-0	HIGH	S.
TRIETHYLAMINE-TETRAMINE	2259	112-24-3	C. LIQ. 1.0	---	LOW	0%
TRIISOBUTYL ALUMINUM	1930	100-99-2	C. LIQ. < 1	3-4-3 W̶	LOW	DEC.
TRIMETHOXY SILANE ***	9269	2487-90-3	C. LIQ. < 1	3-3-2	HIGH	DEC.
TRIMETHYLAMINE ***	1083 1297	75-50-3	C. GAS	3-4-0	GAS	S.
TRIMETHYL BORATE	2416	121-43-7	C. LIQ. < 1	2-3-1	---	DEC.

PPE	INCOMPATIBILITIES	SPILL	DECON.	FIRE	FIRST AID	SPECIAL
LEVEL A ---	OXIDIZERS	S1,S7	SOAP	F1,F7, F9	H6,H7, H8,H9	E1,E9
LEVEL B NIT(0)	OXIDIZERS,Cu	S1,S7	WATER	F1,F7, F9	H6,H7, H8,H9	E2,E9
LEVEL A ---	OXIDIZERS,WATER, ALCOHOLS	S3,S6, S7	WATER	F1,F7, F9	H6,H7, H8,H9	E2,E7,E9, E12
LEVEL B TEF(-)	OXIDIZERS	S3,S7	SOAP	F1,F7, F9	H9	E1,E9
LEVEL B VIN(+) VIT(+)	OXIDIZERS,Al,Mg,Ba, Ti,ALKALI, ALKALI METALS	S1,S6, S7,S8	SOAP	F1,F7, F9	H1,H9	E1,E3,E6, E9
LEVEL B ---	COMBUSTIBLES, AMINES, REDUCING AGENTS	S3,S7	WATER	F4,F7, F9	H6,H7, H8,H9	E1,E9,E13, E16
LEVEL A ---	OXIDIZERS	S3,S7, S8	WATER	F1,F7, F9	H2,H9	E1,E9
LEVEL A ---	AIR,WATER, OXIDIZERS, COMBUSTIBLES	S9	DRY	F3,F7, F8,F9, F14	H6,H7, H8,H9	E2,E4,E7,E9, E11,E16
LEVEL B NIT(+) VIT(+) SAR(+)	OXIDIZERS	S1,S6, S7	SOAP	F1,F7, F9	H6,H7, H8,H9	E1,E3,E4, E9
LEVEL B ---	OXIDIZERS	S1,S7	SOAP	F1,F7, F9	H6,H7, H8,H9	E1,E9
LEVEL A ---	WATER,ACIDS,AIR, HALOGENS, COMBUSTIBLES	S9	DRY	F5,F7, F8,F9, F12, F14	H6,H7, H8,H9	E2,E3,E4,E7, E9,E11,E12 E16
LEVEL B ---	WATER,ALKALI, ACIDS,ALCOHOLS	S1,S6, S7	BASE	F1,F7, F9	H9	E1,E3,E9, E14
LEVEL B ---	OXIDIZERS,Hg, HALOCARBONS, HALOGENS,ACIDS	S2,S5, S6	WATER	F1,F7, F9,F10	H6,H7, H8,H9	E1,E3,E4, E9
LEVEL B ---	OXIDIZERS	S1,S7	WATER	F2,F7, F9	H9	E1,E3,E9

CHEMICAL NAME	DOT #	CAS #	FORM	NFPA	VAPOR PRESS.	WATER SOL.
TRIMETHYL-CHLOROSILANE	1298	75-77-4	C. LIQ. < 1	3-3-2 ₩	HIGH	DEC.
TRIMETHYL PHOSPHITE	2329	121-45-9	C. LIQ. < 1	0-2-0	MOD.	0%
TRIPROPYL-ALUMINUM	2718	102-67-0	C. LIQ. < 1	---	LOW	DEC.
TRIPROPYL-AMINE	2260	102-69-2	C. LIQ. < 1	2-2-0	LOW	< 1%
TURPENTINE	1299	8006-64-2	C. LIQ. < 1	1-3-0	MOD.	0%
VALERYL CHLORIDE	2502	638-29-9	C. LIQ. 1.0	---	---	DEC.
VANADIUM OXYTRICHLORIDE	2443	7727-18-6	YELL. LIQ. > 1	---	MOD.	DEC.
VANADIUM PENTOXIDE ***	2862	1314-62-1	YELL. POWD.	---	NONE	< 1%
VANADIUM TETRACHLORIDE	2444	7632-51-1	RED LIQ. > 1	3-0-2 ₩	---	DEC.
VINYL ACETATE ***	1301	108-05-4	C. LIQ. < 1	2-3-2	HIGH	0%
VINYL BROMIDE	1085	593-60-2	C. GAS	2-0-1	GAS	0%
VINYL CHLORIDE ***	1086	75-01-4	C. GAS	2-4-2	GAS	0%
VINYLIDINE CHLORIDE ***	1303	75-35-4	C. LIQ. > 1	2-4-2	HIGH	0%
VINYL TOLUENE	2618	25013-15-4	C. LIQ. < 1	2-2-2	LOW	0%

PPE	INCOMPATIBILITIES	SPILL	DECON.	FIRE	FIRST AID	SPECIAL
LEVEL A ---	OXIDIZERS, WATER	S1,S6, S7	DRY	F2,F7, F8,F9	H6,H7, H8,H9	E1,E3,E7, E9,E12
LEVEL B ---	OXIDIZERS	S1,S6, S7	SOAP	F1,F7, F9	H6,H7, H8,H9	E1,E3,E7,E9
LEVEL A ---	AIR,O₂,WATER, HALOCARBONS, ACIDS,ALCOHOLS	S9	DRY	F5,F7, F8,F9, F13	H6,H7, H8,H9	E2,E3,E7,E9, E11,E12,E16
LEVEL B NEO(+) NIT(+) VIN(+) VIT(+)	OXIDIZERS	S1,S7	SOAP	F1,F7, F9	H9	E1,E3,E9
LEVEL B VIN(+) TEF(0)	OXIDIZERS	S1,S6, S7	SOAP	F1,F7	H9	E1,E3
LEVEL B ---	OXIDIZERS,WATER, ALCOHOLS	S1,S7	BASE	F1,F7	H8,H9	E1,E3,E7, E12
LEVEL B ---	ACIDS,WATER, ALCOHOLS, ALKALI METALS	S1,S6, S7	DRY	F3,F7, F8,F9, F13, F14	H6,H7, H8,H9	E1,E3,E7, E9,E12,E16
LEVEL A ---	ALKALI METALS, OXIDIZERS	S3,S7	SOAP	F1,F7, F9	H3,H4, H9	E2,E9
LEVEL A ---	WATER	S3,S7	DRY	F3,F7, F8,F9, F14	H6,H7, H8,H9	E2,E7,E12
LEVEL B ---	OXIDIZERS,LIGHT, ACIDS,AMINES	S1,S6, S7	SOAP	F1,F7, F9	H9	E1,E3,E4, E5,E6,E16
LEVEL B ---	LIGHT,OXIDIZERS, Cu and ALLOYS	S2,S5, S6	---	F1,F7	H1,H9	E1,E3,E4, E5,E6,E16
LEVEL B NIT(0) VIT(0)	OXIDIZERS,Cu,Al, STEEL	S2,S5, S6,S8	---	F1,F7	H2,H9	E1,E3,E4, E5,E6,E16
LEVEL A VIN(0) TEF(0)	OXIDIZERS,ACIDS, Cu and ALLOYS, Al and ALLOYS	S1,S6, S7,S8	SOAP	F2,F7, F9	H1,H9	E1,E3,E4, E5,E6,E16
LEVEL A ---	OXIDIZERS,ACIDS, METAL SALTS	S1,S7	SOAP	F1,F7, F9	H9	E1,F3,F4, E5,E6,E16

CHEMICAL NAME	DOT #	CAS #	FORM	NFPA	VAPOR PRESS.	WATER SOL.
XYLENE ***	1307	1330-20-7	C. LIQ. < 1	2-3-0	MOD.	0%
o-XYLIDINE	1711	87-59-2	YELL. POWD.	3-1-0	---	0%
ZINC CHLORATE	1513	10361-95-2	WHITE POWD.	1-0-1 OX	NONE	S.
ZINC CHLORIDE ***	1840 2331	7646-85-7	WHITE POWD.	---	NONE	S.
ZINC NITRATE ***	1514	7779-88-6	WHITE POWD.	---	NONE	S.
ZINC PHOSPHIDE ***	1714	1314-84-7	GREY POWD.	3-3-1	LOW	0%
ZIRCONIUM	1308 1358 2008 2009 2858	7440-67-7	GREY METAL	---	NONE	0%
ZIRCONIUM TETRACHLORIDE	2503	10026-11-6	WHITE POWD.	3-0-2 W	LOW	DEC.

PPE	INCOMPATIBILITIES	SPILL	DECON.	FIRE	FIRST AID	SPECIAL
LEVEL B VIN(+) VIT(+) TEF(0)	OXIDIZERS	S1,S6, S7,S8	SOAP	F1,F7	H6,H9	E1,E3
LEVEL A ---	OXIDIZERS	S3,S7	SOAP	F1,F7, F9	H6,H7, H8,H9, H12	E2,E9
LEVEL B ---	Al,Cu,P,As,S,ACIDS, COMBUSTIBLES, SULFIDES,MnO₂	S3,S7	SOAP	F4,F7, F9	H6,H8, H9	E2,E9,E13
LEVEL B ---	ALKALI METALS	S3,S7	SOAP	F1,F7, F9	H1,H6, H7,H8, H9	E2,E9
LEVEL B ---	COMBUSTIBLES, SULFIDES,P,S,Al, REDUCING AGENTS	S3,S7	WATER	F4,F7	H6,H7, H8,H9	E1,E9,E13
LEVEL A ---	ACIDS, OXIDIZERS	S3,S7, S8	SOAP	F5,F7, F9	H6,H7, H8,H9	E2,E7,E9
LEVEL B ---	MATERIAL REACTS WITH NUMEROUS MATERIALS	S3,S7	SOAP	F5,F7, F14	H9	E1,E7,E11, E16
LEVEL B ---	ACIDS, AMINES, AIR, ALCOHOLS	S3,S7	DRY	F2,F7, F8,F9	H5,H6, H7,H8, H9	E1,E7,E9, E11,E16

SECTION TWO

ISOLATION DISTANCES
AND
REPORTING INFORMATION

CHEMICAL NAME	DOT ISOLATION	DOT TAKE COVER	RCRA WASTE #	REPORTABLE QUANTITIES
ACETAL	---	---	U001	1000 lb 1000 lb
ACETIC ACID	---	---	---	5000 lb 1000 lb
ACETIC ANHYDRIDE	---	---	---	5000 lb 1000 lb
ACETONE	---	---	U002	5000 lb 1 lb
ACETONE CYANOHYDRIN	150 ft 150 ft	0.2 miles 0.2 miles	P069	10 lb 10 lb
ACETONITRILE	---	---	U003	5000 lb 1 lb
ACETYL BROMIDE	---	---	---	5000 lb 5000 lb
ACETYL CHLORIDE	---	---	U006	5000 lb 5000 lb
ACROLEIN	900 ft 1200 ft	3 miles 4 miles	P003	1 lb 1 lb
ACRYLAMIDE	---	---	U007	5000 lb 1 lb
ACRYLIC ACID	---	---	U008	5000 lb 1 lb
ACRYLONITRILE	---	---	U009	100 lb 100 lb
ALDRIN	---	---	P004	1 lb 1 lb
ALLYL ALCOHOL	150 ft 150 ft	0.8 miles 0.8 miles	P005	100 lb 100lb
ALLYL AMINE	150 ft 600 ft	0.8 miles 2 miles	---	---
ALLYL CHLORIDE	---	---	---	1000 lb 1000 lb
ALLYL CHLOROCARBONATE	150 ft 150 ft	0.2 miles 0.2 miles	---	---
ALUMINUM PHOSPHIDE	---	---	P006	100 lb 1 lb
AMMONIA	150 ft 300 ft	0.2 miles 1 mile	---	100 lb 100 lb
AMMONIUM BIFLUORIDE	---	---	---	100 lb 5000 lb

CHEMICAL NAME	DOT ISOLATION	DOT TAKE COVER	RCRA WASTE #	REPORTABLE QUANTITIES
AMMONIUM FLUORIDE	---	---	---	100 lb 5000 lb
AMMONIUM PICRATE	---	---	P009	10 lb 1 lb
AMMONIUM VANADATE	---	---	P119	1000 lb 1 lb
AMYL ACETATE	---	---	---	5000 lb 100 lb
ANILINE	---	---	U012	5000 lb 1000 lb
ANTIMONY	---	---	---	5000 lb 1 lb
ANTIMONY PENTACHLORIDE	---	---	---	1000 lb 1000 lb
ANTIMONY TRICHLORIDE	---	---	---	1000 lb 1000 lb
ARSENIC	---	---	---	1 lb 1 lb
ARSENIC ACID	---	---	P010	1 lb 1 lb
ARSENIC TRISULFIDE	---	---	---	1 lb 5000 lb
ARSENIC TRICHLORIDE	1200 ft 1500 ft	4 miles 5 miles	---	1 lb 5000 lb
ARSENIC TRIOXIDE	---	---	P012	1 lb 5000 lb
ARSINE	1500 ft 1500 ft	5 miles 5 miles	---	---
BARIUM CYANIDE	---	---	P013	10 lb 10 lb
BENZENE	---	---	U109	10 lb 1000 lb
BENZENE SULFONYL CHLORIDE	---	---	U020	100 lb 1 lb
BENZIDINE	---	---	U021	1 lb 1 lb
BENZONITRILE	---	---	---	5000 lb 1000 lb
BENZOQUINONE	---	---	U197	10 lb 1 lb

CHEMICAL NAME	DOT ISOLATION	DOT TAKE COVER	RCRA WASTE #	REPORTABLE QUANTITIES
BENZOTRICHLORIDE	---	---	U203	10 lb 1 lb
BENZOYL CHLORIDE	---	---	---	1000 lb 1000 lb
BENZYL CHLORIDE	---	---	P028	100 lb 100 lb
BERYLLIUM	---	---	P015	10 lb 1 lb
BERYLLIUM FLUORIDE	---	---	---	1 lb 5000 lb
BERYLLIUM NITRATE	---	---	---	1 lb 5000 lb
BIS(CHLOROMETHYL) ETHER	---	---	P016	10 lb 1 lb
1,1-BIS(4-CHLORO-PHENYL)-2,2-DICHLOROETHANE	---	---	U060	1 lb 1 lb
BORON TRIBROMIDE	600 ft 900 ft	2 miles 3 miles	---	---
BORON TRICHLORIDE	600 ft 1500 ft	2 miles 5 miles	---	---
BORON TRIFLUORIDE	1500 ft 1500 ft	5 miles 5 miles	---	---
BROMINE	1500 ft 1500 ft	5 miles 5 miles		---
BROMINE PENTAFLUORIDE	1500 ft 1500 ft	5 miles 5 miles	---	---
BROMINE TRIFLUORIDE	150 ft 150 ft	0.8 miles 0.8 miles	---	---
BROMOACETONE	150 ft 150 ft	0.2 miles 0.2 miles	P017	1000 lb 1 lb
BROMOFORM	---	---	U225	100 lb 1 lb
BRUCINE	---	---	P018	100 lb 1 lb
1-BUTANOL	---	---	U031	5000 lb 1 lb
n-BUTYL ACETATE	---	---	---	5000 lb 5000 lb

CHEMICAL NAME	DOT ISOLATION	DOT TAKE COVER	RCRA WASTE #	REPORTABLE QUANTITIES
n-BUTYLAMINE	---	---	---	1000 lb 1000 lb
n-BUTYL ISOCYANATE	150 ft 150 ft	0.8 miles 0.8 miles	---	---
BUTYRIC ACID	---	---	---	5000 lb 5000 lb
CACODYLIC ACID	---	---	U136	1 lb 1 lb
CADMIUM CHLORIDE	---	---	---	10 lb 100 lb
CALCIUM CARBIDE	---	---	---	10 lb 5000 lb
CALCIUM CYANIDE	---	---	P021	10 lb 10 lb
CARBARYL	---	---	---	100 lb 100 lb
CARBOFURAN	---	---	---	10 lb 10 lb
CARBON DISULFIDE	---	---	P022	100 lb 5000 lb
CARBON MONOXIDE	1500 ft 1500 ft	5 miles 5 miles	---	---
CARBON TETRACHLORIDE	---	---	U211	10 lb 5000 lb
CARBONYL FLUORIDE	1500 ft 1500 ft	5 miles 5 miles	U033	1000 lb 1 lb
CARBONYL SULFIDE	600 ft 600 ft	2 miles 2 miles	---	---
CHLORDANE	---	---	U036	1 lb 1 lb
CHLORONATED CAMPHENE	---	---	D015	1 lb 1 lb
CHLORINE	900 ft 1500 ft	3 miles 5 miles	---	10 lb 10 lb
CHLORINE DIOXIDE	1500 ft 1500 ft	5 miles 5 miles	---	---
CHLORINE PENTAFLUORIDE	900 ft 1500 ft	3 miles 5 miles	---	---
CHLOROACET-ALDEHYDE	---	---	P023	1000 lb 1 lb

CHEMICAL NAME	DOT ISOLATION	DOT TAKE COVER	RCRA WASTE #	REPORTABLE QUANTITIES
CHLOROACETIC ACID	150 ft 150 ft	0.2 miles 0.2 miles	---	---
CHLOROACETONE	150 ft 150 ft	0.2 miles 0.2 miles	---	---
CHLORO-ACETOPHENONE	900 ft 1200 ft	3 miles 4 miles	---	---
4-CHLOROANILINE	---	---	P024	1000 lb 1 lb
CHLOROFORM	---	---	U044	10 lb 5000 lb
CHLOROPICRIN	600 ft 900 ft	2 miles 3 miles	---	---
CHLOROPIVOYL-CHLORIDE	150 ft 150 ft	0.2 miles 0.2 miles	---	---
CHLOROSULFONIC ACID	150 ft 150 ft	0.2 miles 0.2 miles	---	1000 lb 1000 lb
CHLORPYRIFOS®	---	---	---	1 lb 1 lb
CHROMIC ACID	---	---	---	10 lb 1000 lb
CHROMIC NITRATE	---	---	---	--- 1 lb
CHROMYL CHLORIDE	---	---	---	--- 1 lb
COPPER (II) CYANIDE	---	---	P029	10 lb 1 lb
COPPER (II) NITRATE	***	***	---	100 lb 100 lb
m-CRESOL	---	---	U052	1000 lb 1000 lb
CROTONALDEHYDE	150 ft 150 ft	0.2 miles 0.4 miles	U053	100 lb 100 lb
CUMENE	---	---	U055	5000 lb 1 lb
CYANOGEN	300 ft 300 ft	1 mile 1 mile	P031	100 lb 1 lb
CYANOGEN BROMIDE	900 ft 900 ft	3 miles 3 miles	U246	1000 lb 1 lb
CYANOGEN CHLORIDE	1500 ft 1500 ft	5 miles 5 miles	P033	10 lb 10 lb

CHEMICAL NAME	DOT ISOLATION	DOT TAKE COVER	RCRA WASTE #	REPORTABLE QUANTITIES
CYCLOHEXANE	---	---	U056	1000 lb 1000 lb
CYCLOHEXANONE	---	---	U057	5000 lb 1 lb
2,4-D	---	---	U240	100 lb 100 lb
DDT	---	---	U061	1 lb 1 lb
DIAZINON	---	---	---	1 lb 1 lb
DIBORANE	1500 ft 1500 ft	5 miles 5 miles	---	---
1,2-DIBROMO-3-CHLOROPROPANE	---	---	U066	1 lb 1 lb
1,2-DIBROMO-ETHANE	150 ft 150 ft	0.2 miles 0.2 miles	---	---
o-DICHLORO-BENZENE	---	---	U070	100 lb 100 lb
DICHLORODIETHYL ETHER	150 ft 150 ft	0.2 miles 0.2 miles	---	---
DICHLORO-DIFLUOROMETHANE	---	---	U075	5000 lb 1 lb
1,1-DICHLORO-ETHANE	---	---	U076	1000 lb 1 lb
1,2-DICHLORO-ETHYLENE	---	---	U079	1000 lb 1 lb
DICHLORO-ISOPROPYL ETHER	---	---	U027	1000 lb 1 lb
1,3-DICHLORO-PROPENE	---	---	U084	100 lb 5000 lb
2,2-DICHLORO-PROPIONIC ACID	---	---	---	5000 lb 5000 lb
DICHLOROSILANE	300 ft 1200 ft	1 mile 4 miles	---	---
3,5-DICHLORO-2,4,6-TRIFLUORO-PYRIDINE	150 ft 150 ft	0.2 miles 0.2 miles	---	---
DICHLORVOS®	---	---	---	10 lb 10 lb

CHEMICAL NAME	DOT ISOLATION	DOT TAKE COVER	RCRA WASTE #	REPORTABLE QUANTITIES
DIELDRIN®	---	---	P037	1 lb 1 lb
DIETHYLAMINE	---	---	---	100 lb 1000 lb
DIKETENE	150 ft 600 ft	0.8 miles 2 miles	---	---
DIMETHYLAMINE	---	---	U092	1000 lb 1000 lb
DIMETHYL-CARBAMOYL CHLORIDE	---	---	U097	1 lb 1 lb
DIMETHYL CHLOROTHIO-PHOSPHATE	150 ft 150 ft	0.2 miles 0.2 miles	---	---
1,1-DIMETHYL-HYDRAZINE	1200 ft 1500 ft	4 miles 5 miles	U098	10 lb 1 lb
DIMETHYL SULFATE	150 ft 150 ft	0.4 miles 0.4 miles	U103	100 lb 1 lb
1,3-DINITRO-BENZENE	---	---	---	100 lb 1000 lb
DINITRO-o-CRESOL	---	---	P047	10 lb 1 lb
2,4-DINITRO-PHENOL	---	---	P048	10 lb 1000 lb
2,4-DINITRO-TOLUENE	---	---	U105	10 lb 1000 lb
DIOXANE	---	---	U108	100 lb 1 lb
ENDRIN®	---	---	P051	1 lb 1 lb
EPICHLORO-HYDRIN	---	---	U041	100 lb 1000 lb
ETHION	---	---	---	10 lb 10 lb
ETHYL ACETATE	---	---	U112	5000 lb 1 lb
ETHYL ACRYLATE	---	---	U113	1000 lb 1 lb
ETHYLBENZENE	---	---	---	1000 lb 1000 lb

CHEMICAL NAME	DOT ISOLATION	DOT TAKE COVER	RCRA WASTE #	REPORTABLE QUANTITIES
ETHYL CHLOROFORMATE	150 ft 150 ft	0.2 miles 0.2 miles	---	---
ETHYLENE CHLOROHYDRIN	150 ft 150 ft	0.8 miles 0.8 miles	---	---
ETHYLENE DIAMINE	---	---	---	5000 lb 1000 lb
ETHYLENE DICHLORIDE	---	---	U077	100 lb 500 lb
ETHYLENEIMINE600	600 ft 900 ft	2 miles 3 miles	P054	1 lb 1 lb
ETHYLENE OXIDE	150 ft 600 ft	0.8 miles 2 miles	U115	10 lb 1 lb
ETHYL ISOCYANATE	150 ft 150 ft	0.8 miles 0.8 miles	---	---
FERRIC CHLORIDE	---	---	---	1000 lb 1000 lb
FLUORINE	1500 ft 1500 ft	5 miles 5 miles	P056	10 lb 1 lb
FORMALDEHYDE	600 ft 600 ft	2 miles 2 miles	U122	100 lb 1000 lb
FORMIC ACID	---	---	U123	5000 lb 5000 lb
FURAN	---	---	U124	100 lb 1 lb
FURFURAL	---	---	U125	5000 lb 1000 lb
GERMANE	1500 ft 1500 ft	5 miles 5 miles	---	---
HEXACHLORO- BENZENE	---	---	U127	10 lb 1 lb
HEXACHLORO- BUTADIENE	---	---	U128	1 lb 1 lb
HEXACHLORO- CYCLOPENTADIENE	150 ft 150 ft	0.4 miles 0.4 miles	U130	10 lb 1 lb
HEXACHLORO- ETHANE	---	---	U131	100 lb 1 lb
HEXAFLUORO- ACETONE	1500 ft 1500 ft	5 miles 5 miles	---	---
HYDRAZINE	---	---	U133	1 lb 1 lb

CHEMICAL NAME	DOT ISOLATION	DOT TAKE COVER	RCRA WASTE #	REPORTABLE QUANTITIES
HYDROGEN BROMIDE	1500 ft 1500 ft	5 miles 5 miles	---	---
HYDROGEN CHLORIDE	1200 ft 1500 ft	4 miles 5 miles	---	5000 lb 5000 lb
HYDROGEN CYANIDE	600 ft 600 ft	2 miles 2 miles	P063	10 lb 10 lb
HYDROGEN FLUORIDE	300 ft 900 ft	1 mile 3 miles	U134	100 lb 5000 lb
HYDROGEN SELENIDE	1500 ft 1500 ft	5 miles 5 miles	---	---
HYDROGEN SULFIDE	1500 ft 1500 ft	5 miles 5 miles	---	---
IRON PENTACARBONYL	1500 ft 1500 ft	5 miles 5 miles	---	---
ISOPHORONE DIISOCYANATE	900 ft 900 ft	3 miles 3 miles	---	---
ISOPRENE	---	---	---	100 lb 1000 lb
ISOPROPYL-CHLOROFORMATE	150 ft 150 ft	0.2 miles 0.2 miles	---	---
LEAD ARSENATE	---	---	---	1 lb 5000 lb
LEAD NITRATE	---	---	---	100 lb 5000 lb
MALATHION®	---	---	---	100 lb 10 lb
MALEIC ANHYDRIDE	---	---	U147	5000 lb 5000 lb
MALONITRILE	---	---	U149	1000 lb 1 lb
MERCURIC ACETATE	---	---	---	--- 1 lb
MERCURIC CYANIDE	---	---	---	1 lb 1 lb
MERCURIC NITRATE	---	---	---	10 lb 10 lb
MERCURY	---	---	U151	1 lb 1 lb
METHACRYLO-NITRILE	---	---	U152	1000 lb 1 lb

CHEMICAL NAME	DOT ISOLATION	DOT TAKE COVER	RCRA WASTE #	REPORTABLE QUANTITIES
METHANOL	---	---	U154	5000 lb 1 lb
METHYLAMINE	150 ft 900 ft	0.8 miles 3 miles	---	---
METHYL BROMIDE	600 ft 900 ft	2 miles 3 miles	U029	1000 lb 1 lb
METHYL CHLORIDE	---	---	U045	100 lb 1 lb
METHYL CHLORO-CARBONATE	150 ft 600 ft	0.8 miles 2 miles	U156	1000 lb 1 lb
METHYL CHLOROFORM	---	---	U226	1000 lb 1 lb
METHYL CHLORO-METHYL ETHER	150 ft 150 ft	0.2 miles 0.4 miles	---	---
METHYL HYDRAZINE	1500 ft 1500 ft	5 miles 5 miles	P068	10 lb 1 lb
METHYL IODIDE	---	---	U138	100 lb 1 lb
METHYL ISOCYANATE	1500 ft 1500 ft	5 miles 5 miles	P064	1 lb 1 lb
METHYL MERCAPTAN	150 ft 600 ft	0.8 miles 2 miles	U153	100 lb 100 lb
METHYL METHACRYLATE	---	---	U162	1000 lb 5000 lb
METHYL PARATHION	---	---	P071	100 lb 100 lb
METHYLPHOS-PHONIC DICHLORIDE	150 ft 150 ft	0.2 miles 0.2 miles	---	---
MEVINPHOS®	---	---	---	10 lb 1 lb
NAPHTHALENE	---	---	U165	100 lb 5000 lb
1-NAPHTHYLAMINE	---	---	U167	100 lb 1 lb
1-NAPHTHYL-THIOUREA	---	---	P072	100 lb 1 lb
NICKEL CARBONYL	1500 ft 1500 ft	5 miles 5 miles	P073	10 lb 1 lb
NICOTINE	---	---	P075	100 lb 1 lb

CHEMICAL NAME	DOT ISOLATION	DOT TAKE COVER	RCRA WASTE #	REPORTABLE QUANTITIES
NITRIC ACID	---	---	---	1000 lb 1000 lb
FUMING NITRIC ACID	150 ft 150 ft	0.8 miles 0.8 miles	---	1000 lb 1000 lb
NITRIC OXIDE	600 ft 900 ft	2 miles 3 miles	P076	10 lb 1 lb
p-NITROANILINE	---	---	P077	5000 lb 1 lb
NITROBENZENE	---	---	U169	1000 lb 1000 lb
NITROGEN DIOXIDE	150 ft 600 ft	0.8 miles 2 miles	P078	10 lb 1000 lb
NITROGEN TRIFLUORIDE	150 ft 150 ft	0.4 miles 0.8 miles	---	---
p NITROPHENOL	---	---	U170	100 lb 1000 lb
NITROPROPANE	---	---	U171	10 lb 1 lb
NITROSYL CHLORIDE	150 ft 600 ft	0.4 miles 2 miles	---	---
tert-OCTYL-MERCAPTAN	150 ft 150 ft	0.2 miles 0.2 miles	---	---
OSMIUM TETROXIDE	---	---	P087	1000 lb 1 lb
PARALDEHYDE	---	---	U182	1000 lb 1 lb
PARATHION	---	---	P089	10 lb 1 lb
PENTABORANE	1500 ft 1500 ft	5 miles 5 miles	---	---
PENTACHLORO-ETHANE	---	---	U184	10 lb 1 lb
PERCHLORO-ETHYLENE	---	---	U210	100 lb 1 lb
PERCHLORO-METHYL MERCAPTAN	150 ft 150 ft	0.8 miles 0.8 miles	P118	100 lb 1 lb
PERCHLORYL FLUORIDE	900 ft 900 ft	3 miles 3 miles	---	---
PHENOL	---	---	U188	1000 lb 1000 lb

CHEMICAL NAME	DOT ISOLATION	DOT TAKE COVER	RCRA WASTE #	REPORTABLE QUANTITIES
PHENYL ISOCYANATE	150 ft 150 ft	0.2 miles 0.2 miles	---	---
PHENYL MERCAPTAN	150 ft 150 ft	0.2 miles 0.2 miles	P014	100 lb 1 lb
PHOSGENE	1500 ft 1500 ft	5 miles 5 miles	P095	10 lb 5000 lb
PHOSPHINE	1500 ft 1500 ft	5 miles 5 miles	P096	100 lb 1 lb
PHOSPHORUS	---	---	---	1 lb 1 lb
PHOSPHORUS OXYCHLORIDE	600 ft 900 ft	2 miles 3 miles	---	1000 lb 5000 lb
PHOSPHORUS PENTASULFIDE	---	---	U189	100 lb 100 lb
PHOSPHORUS TRICHLORIDE	900 ft 1500 ft	3 miles 5 miles	---	1000 lb 5000 lb
PHTHALIC ANHYDRIDE	---	---	U190	5000 lb 1 lb
POTASSIUM CYANIDE	---	---	P098	10 lb 10 lb
POTASSIUM PERMANGANATE	---	---	---	100 lb 100 lb
PROPARGYL ALCOHOL	---	---	P102	1000 lb 1 lb
PROPIONIC ACID	---	---	---	5000 lb 5000 lb
PROPIONIC ANHYDRIDE	---	---	---	5000 lb 5000 lb
PROPIONITRILE	---	---	P101	10 lb 1 lb
PROPYLENE DICHLORIDE	---	---	U083	1000 lb 5000 lb
PROPYLENE IMINE	---	---	P067	1 lb 1 lb
PROPYLENE OXIDE	---	---	---	100 lb 5000 lb
PYRIDINE	---	---	U196	1000 lb 1 lb
QUINOLINE	---	---	---	5000 lb 1000 lb

CHEMICAL NAME	DOT ISOLATION	DOT TAKE COVER	RCRA WASTE #	REPORTABLE QUANTITIES
RESORCINOL	---	---	U201	5000 lb 1000 lb
SELENIUM	---	---	---	100 lb 1 lb
SELENIUM HEXAFLUORIDE	1500 ft 1500 ft	5 miles 5 miles	---	---
SILICON TETRAFLUORIDE	1200 ft 1500 ft	4 miles 5 miles	---	---
SILVER NITRATE	---	---	---	1 lb 1 lb
SODIUM	---	---	---	10 lb 1000 lb
SODIUM AZIDE	---	---	P105	1000 lb 1 lb
SODIUM CYANIDE	---	---	P106	10 lb 10 lb
SODIUM FLUORIDE	---	---	---	1000 lb 5000 lb
SODIUM HYDROSULFIDE	---	---	---	5000 lb 5000 lb
SODIUM HYDROXIDE	---	---	---	1000 lb 1000 lb
SODIUM METHYLATE	---	---	---	1000 lb 1000 lb
SODIUM NITRITE	---	---	---	100 lb 100 lb
SODIUM SELENATE	---	---	---	100 lb 1000 lb
STIBINE	1500 ft 1500 ft	5 miles 5 miles	---	---
STRYCHNINE	---	---	P108	10 lb 10 lb
STYRENE	---	---	---	1000 lb 1000 lb
SULFUR CHLORIDE	600 ft 600 ft	2 miles 2 miles	---	1000 lb 1000 lb
SULFUR DIOXIDE	600 ft 1500 ft	2 miles 5 miles	---	---
SULFURIC ACID	150 ft 150 ft	0.4 miles 0.4 miles	---	1000 lb 1000 lb

CHEMICAL NAME	DOT ISOLATION	DOT TAKE COVER	RCRA WASTE #	REPORTABLE QUANTITIES
SULFUR TRIOXIDE	150 ft 150 ft	0.4 miles 0.8 miles	---	---
SULFURYL FLUORIDE	900 ft 1500 ft	3 miles 5 miles	---	---
2,4,5-T	---	---	U232	1000 lb 100 lb
TETRACHLORO-ETHANE	---	---	U209	100 lb 1 lb
TETRAETHYL LEAD	---	---	P110	10 lb 100 lb
TETRAETHYL PYROPHOSPHATE	---	---	P111	10 lb 100 lb
TETRAMETHYL ORTHOSILICATE	150 ft 150 ft	0.4 miles 0.8 miles	---	---
TETRANITRO-METHANE	150 ft 150 ft	0.4 miles 0.8 miles	P112	10 lb 1 lb
THALLIUM NITRATE	---	---	U217	100 lb 1 lb
TITANIUM TETRACHLORIDE	150 ft 150 ft	0.2 miles 0.2 miles	---	---
TOLUENE	---	---	U220	1000 lb 1000 lb
TOLUENE-2,4-DIAMINE	---	---	U221	10 lb 1 lb
TOLUENE 2,4-DIISOCYANATE	---	---	U223	100 lb 1 lb
o-TOLUIDINE	---	---	U328	100 lb 1 lb
TRIBUTYLAMINE	150 ft 150 ft	0.2 miles 0.2 miles	---	---
1,2,4-TRICHLORO-BENZENE	---	---	---	100 lb 1 lb
TRICHLORO-ETHYLENE	---	---	U228	100 lb 1000 lb
2,4,6-TRICHLORO-PHENOL	---	---	U231	10 lb 10 lb
TRIETHYLAMINE	---	---	---	5000 lb 5000 lb
TRIMETHOXY-SILANE	150 ft 150 ft	0.4 miles 0.8 miles	---	---

CHEMICAL NAME	DOT ISOLATION	DOT TAKE COVER	RCRA WASTE #	REPORTABLE QUANTITIES
TRIMETHYLAMINE	---	---	---	100 lb 1000 lb
VANADIUM PENTOXIDE	---	---	P120	1000 lb 1000 lb
VINYL ACETATE	---	---	---	5000 lb 100 lb
VINYL CHLORIDE	---	---	U043	1 lb 1 lb
VINYLIDINE CHLORIDE	---	---	U078	100 lb 5000 lb
XYLENE	---	---	U239	1000 lb 1000 lb
ZINC CHLORIDE	---	---	---	1000 lb 5000 lb
ZINC NITRATE	---	---	---	1000 lb 5000 lb
ZINC PHOSPHIDE	---	---	P122	100 lb 1000 lb

FIRE FIGHTING CODES
FIRST AID CODES
SPECIAL HAZARD CODES
DEFINITIONS AND ABBREVIATIONS
INDEX OF DOT NUMBERS

Fire Fighting Codes

F1: Foam, water, carbon dioxide, or dry chemical may be used to extinguish fire.

F2: Alcohol-resistant foam, water, carbon dioxide, or dry chemical may be used to extinguish fire.

F3: Dry chemical or carbon dioxide only should be used to extinguish fire.

F4: Water should be used to extinguish fire.

F5: Fire should be smothered using dry sand, clay, or Class D extinguisher.

F6: Use extinguishing agent suitable for surrounding fire.

F7: If possible, fight fires from a protected location. Water spray should be used to keep containers cool. Immediately withdraw if rising sound from venting device is heard or if fire is causing discoloration of the tank. For large fires, withdraw and allow to burn. Isolate for 1/2 mile if rail or tank car is involved in fire.

F8: Do not allow water to enter container.

F9: Structural firefighter's protective clothing may not provide adequate protection.

F10: Containers may rupture upon heating.

F11: Water spray from an unmanned device should be used to keep closed containers cool. Continue to cool after fire is extinguished.

F12: If controlled, allow fire to burn.

F13: Do not use water.

F14: Use flooding quantities of water.

F15: Do not use CO_2.

First Aid Codes

H1: Material is a potential carcinogen.

H2: Material is a confirmed carcinogen.

H3: Material may be a mutagen.

H4: Material may be a teratogen.

H5: Exposure may cause an allergic response.

H6: Exposure to material may result in chemical pneumonitis or pulmonary edema.

H7: Inhalation of vapors may be fatal by causing the glottis to spasm, resulting in suffocation.

H8: Contact with material may cause burns to skin, eyes, and upper respiratory tract. Burns may take several days to manifest themselves.

H9: Remove to ventilated area, immediately remove any contaminated clothing and wash contaminated areas with water for a minimum of 15 minutes. Treat supportively and observe for possible shock. If ingested, seek immediate medical aid.

H10: Treat for cyanide poisoning as necessary.

H11: Remove to fresh air and give artificial respiration or oxygen as necessary.

H12: Absorption may lead to the formation of methemoglobin, resulting in cyanosis several hours after exposure.

H13: Contact with liquefied/frozen material may cause frostbite.

H14: Treat for anticholinesterase poisoning.

H15: Vapors may attack eye and mucous membranes to cause permanent structural changes and damage. Effects may be delayed.

Special Hazard Codes

E1: May be harmful if inhaled, swallowed, or absorbed through the skin.

E2: May be fatal if inhaled, swallowed, or absorbed through the skin.

E3: Vapors are heavier than air and may travel some distance to an ignition source. Vapors are more dense than air and may settle in low-lying areas.

E4: This material has an extremely low ignition energy.

E5: May form peroxides upon prolonged exposure to air.

E6: May undergo hazardous polymerization.

E7: May react with incompatible substances to yield toxic products (gases or solution).

E8: Heat, shock, or friction may cause an explosion.

E9: May release toxic substances upon heating.

E10: Material may be formulated with a possibly flammable solvent. Properties of any solvent present should be evaluated prior to any response activities.

E11: Material may be pyrophoric.

E12: Exposure to moist air or water may cause a spontaneous, exothermic reaction.

E13: May oxidize combustibles at elevated temperatures.

E14: Heating may result in violent decomposition.

E15: May become explosively unstable after prolonged storage.

E16: May react explosively with incompatible substances or generate explosive/pyrophoric substances upon exposure to incompatible substances.

E17: May be present in a molten form.

Spill Codes

S1: Remove all potential ignition sources. Absorb with noncombustible absorbant and take up using nonsparking tools.

S2: Remove all ignition sources.

S3: Take up for later disposal.

S4: Cover with sodium bicarbonate, take up, and dispose.

S5: Stop leak if it can safely be done.

S6: Keep area isolated until vapors have dissipated.

S7: Treat all materials used or generated and equipment involved as contaminated by hazardous waste.

S8: Material spilled is an RCRA-listed waste.

S9: Clean up under expert supervision.

S10: Use polyethylene tools.

Definitions and Abbreviations

Acyl Chlorides – Organic acids that have a chlorine present instead of an OH. Examples include acetyl chloride; typically have a "cyl chloride" suffix.

As – Arsenic

Ag – Silver

$AlCl_3$ – Aluminum trichloride

Alkali Metals – Lithium, sodium, potassium, rubidium, cesium, and francium

Alkenes – A class of compounds that contain a carbon-carbon double bond. Names of these materials typically contain an "ene" suffix.

Alkynes – A class of compounds that contain a carbon-carbon triple bond. Names of these materials typically contain an "yne" suffix.

Au – Gold

B – Boron

Ba – Barium

Be – Beryllium

Bi – Bismuth

Br – Bromine

C – Carbon

Ca – Calcium

Carbides – A class of compounds that contain a carbon bound to a metal, such as calcium carbide.

Cd – Cadmium

Ce – Cerium

$CHCl_3$ – Chloroform

Cs – Cesium

Cl – Chlorine

Cr – Chromium

CS_2 – Carbon disulfide

Co – Cobalt

Cu – Copper

Combustibles – Materials containing a carbon-hydrogen bond, such as ordinary combustibles, solvents, waxes, fuels, etc.

DMF – Dimethylformamide

DMSO – Dimethylsulfoxide

F – Fluorine

Fe – Iron

H – Hydrogen

Halides – Salts of halogens, e.g., sodium chloride, silver bromide.

Halogens – Chlorine, fluorine, bromine, and iodine.

Halocarbons – Carbon-containing materials that also have a halogen bond.

Hg – Mercury

I – Iodine

K – Potassium

Li – Lithium

Mg – Magnesium

Mn – Manganese

MnO_2 – Manganese dioxide

Mo – Molybdenum

N – Nitrogen

Na – Sodium

NH_3 – Ammonia

Ni – Nickel

Nitrated Materials – Materials containing an NO_3 group, such as nitrobenzene, nitrocellulose, etc. Many times, these materials have a "nitro" prefix.

Nitriles – A class of compounds containing a carbon-nitrogen triple bond, such as cyanides, acetonitrile, etc.

O – Oxygen

Os – Osmium

Oxides – A class of compounds that contain oxygen. These are typically metal oxides such as iron oxide (rust), manganese dioxide, etc.

Oxidizers – A class of compounds typically able to increase the number of oxygen bonds in other materials. Examples are permanganates, dichromates, peroxides, halogens, oxygen, ozone, etc.

P – Phosphorus

P_2O_5 – Phosphorus pentoxide

Pb – Lead

PbO_2 – Lead dioxide

Pd – Palladium

PH_3 – Phosphine

Pt – Platinum

Reducing Agents – A class of compounds that are typically able to reduce the number of oxygen bonds in another material. Examples of these include hydrides and alkali metals.

S – Sulfur

Sulfides – Materials containing a bound sulfur.

Sb – Antimony

Se – Selenium

Si – Silicon

Sn – Tin

Ti – Titanium

W – Tungsten

Zn – Zinc

Zr – Zirconium

DOT Numbers

0004, 8	1053, 52	1106, 8
0072, 30	1061, 58	1107, 10
0118, 30	1062, 60	1108, 10
0222, 8	1063, 60	1109, 10
0282, 66	1064, 62	1111, 10
0402, 8	1067, 66	1112, 10
1001, 2	1069, 66	1113, 10
1005, 6	1070, 68	1114, 12
1009, 16	1072, 68	1120, 18
1010, 18	1073, 68	1123, 18
1011, 18	1075, 18	1125, 18
1013, 22	1076, 70	1126, 16
1016, 22	1077, 76	1127, 18
1017, 24	1079, 82	1129, 18
1026, 28	1081, 84	1130, 22
1027, 30	1083, 88	1131, 22
1028, 34	1085, 90	1135, 44
1032, 38	1086, 90	1143, 28
1033, 40	1088, 2	1144, 28
1036, 42	1089, 2	1145, 30
1037, 42	1090, 2	1147, 30
1038, 44	1091, 2	1148, 32
1040, 44	1092, 4	1149, 18
1045, 46	1093, 4	1150, 34
1048, 50	1098, 4	1152, 34
1049, 50	1100, 4	1153, 44
1050, 50	1101, 36	1154, 36
1051, 50	1104, 8	1155, 36
1052, 50	1105, 8	1156, 38